Y0-ACA-976

GENETICS AND THE FUTURE OF MAN

Genetics ar

contributors

POLYKARP KUSCH
SHELDON C. REED
BENTLEY GLASS
EDWARD L. TATUM
WILLIAM B. SHOCKLEY
PAUL RAMSEY
KINGSLEY DAVIS

he future of man

A DISCUSSION AT THE NOBEL CONFERENCE
organized by Gustavus Adolphus College, St. Peter, Minnesota, 1965

edited by

JOHN D. ROSLANSKY

Woods Hole, Massachusetts

APPLETON-CENTURY-CROFTS NEW YORK
Division of Meredith Publishing Company

666–1

Library of Congress Catalog Card Number: 66–25456

PRINTED IN THE NETHERLANDS

F 76190

Preface

On May 4, 1963, the first American Memorial to Alfred Nobel was dedicated. Twenty-six Nobel Laureates, the third largest gathering of Nobel Prize winners in history, were present at Gustavus Adolphus College, St. Peter, Minnesota, that day to help dedicate the magnificent new Nobel Hall of Science. Three members of the Nobel Foundation board, including its chairman and director, travelled from Stockholm to participate.

On that occasion plans were initiated to start an annual series of Nobel Conferences at Gustavus Adolphus College as a continuing memorial to the Swedish scientist.

Four Nobel Laureates, the late Dr Philip S. Hench of the Mayo Clinic, Dr Polykarp Kusch of Columbia University, Dr Glenn T. Seaborg, Chairman of the United States Atomic Energy Commission, and Dr Edward L. Tatum of the Rockefeller Institute have served as an advisory committee to the college in planning this series of conferences.

The lectures presented in this volume were delivered at the first Nobel Conference, which was held at Gustavus Adolphus on January 7 and 8, 1965. Among the participants in the conference were four Nobel Laureates. Dr Hench served as honorary chairman, Dr Kusch as moderator and formal lectures were presented by Dr Tatum and Dr William Shockley, Alexander Poniatoff Professor of Engineering Science at Stanford University.

Thus the Nobel Hall of Science and the annual Nobel Conferences serve to honor the memory of Alfred Nobel whose final will reads as follows:

'The whole of my remaining realizable estate shall be dealt with in the following way: The capital shall be invested by my executors in safe securities and shall constitute a fund, the interest on which shall be annually distributed in the form of prizes to those who, during the preceding year, shall have conferred the greatest benefit on mankind. The said interest shall be divided into five equal parts, which shall be apportioned as follows: one part to the person who shall have made the most important discovery or invention within the field of physics; one part to the person who shall have made the most important chemical discovery or improvement; one part to the person who shall have made the most important discovery within the domain of physiology or medicine; one part to the person who shall have produced in the field of literature the most outstanding work of an idealistic tendency; and one part to the person who shall have done the most or the best work to promote fraternity between nations for the abolition or reduction of standing armies and for the holding and promotion of peace congresses...'

EDGAR M. CARLSON, *President*
Gustavus Adolphus College

Editor's Acknowledgement

This book represents a revision of the taped record of the first Nobel Conference held January 7 and 8, 1965. It is a compliment to the advisory committee whose bold and imaginative decision initiated this series with so controversial a subject.

Among the many to be complimented for their assistance in making publication efforts a most pleasant experience, are President Edgar M. Carlson, Vice President Ren E. Anderson and Dr Edward L. Tatum. The cordial concern for the personal comfort of visiting participants during the brief visit shown by the entire college community is warmly acknowledged.

The Hill Foundation in offering financial assistance is to be complimented for their recognition of the need and importance of such a public service to mankind.

The Conference value is due first to the wisdom of the advisory committee and finally to the speakers selected to participate in the forum. The deep concern of the symposiasts for human needs resulted in an enthusiastic, often courageous expression of facts and opinions. Their rewards will be realized primarily if their expressions serve to assist man in a bold examination of the varied and perhaps less obvious problems which demand public attention.

The editor is indebted to the unselfish assistance of his kind wife. Further to the participants, who in the midst of their demanding activities saw fit to offer prompt assistance and continued encouragement at all times. Finally, gratitude is extended to the publishers for their attentive concern and assistance.

JOHN D. ROSLANSKY

Dr Hench receiving Nobel Prize on December 10, 1950 from King Gustaf VI Adolphus (Princess Sibylla, King Gustaf VI Adolphus, Prince Wilhelm, Dr Philip Hench)

Tribute to Dr Philip S. Hench

This first volume of the Nobel Conference Lectures at Gustavus Adolphus College honors the memory of Philip Showalter Hench, winner of the Nobel Prize in Medicine in 1950. He was intimately associated with Gustavus Adolphus College in the development of the Nobel Memorial of which the annual Nobel Conference is a part. He served as Chairman of the Advisory Committee of the Nobel Conference, together with Dr Glenn Seaborg (Chemistry 1951), Dr Polykarp Kusch (Physics 1955), and Dr Edward L. Tatum (Medicine 1958), and was chairman of the first Nobel Conference, the lectures of which are the content of this volume. He died on March 30, 1965.

The 1950 Nobel Prize in Medicine was awarded jointly to Dr Hench, his close associate at the Mayo Clinic, Dr Edward C. Kendall, and Dr Tadeus Reichstein of Switzerland 'for their discoveries relating to the hormones of the adrenal cortex, their structure and biological effects'. His work is more commonly described in terms of his contribution to the discovery and use of cortisone. He was a member of the staff of the Mayo Clinic at Rochester, Minnesota, from 1923, head of the section on Rheumatic Disease from 1926, a teacher in the Mayo Foundation for Medical Education and Research, Graduate School, University of Minnesota since 1928, holding the rank of full professor since 1947.

He was a person of remarkable energy, amazing capacity for friendship, an exceptional breadth of interests, and an almost unlimited array of information on a wide range of subjects. He wrote feature articles for the Metropolitan Opera news bulletin; he was a Conan Doyle enthusiast of sufficient stature to have a display of his materials featured in New York; he was a camera fan of almost mailorder dimensions; he reached out for everyone that his life touched. Together with his wife, Mary Kahler Hench and their four children, he enjoyed life to the full and wasted no part of it.

We are grateful that Gustavus Adolphus College and the Nobel Conference were included within the circle of his interests.

EDGAR M. CARLSON

Contents

POLYKARP KUSCH

Introductory statement

DR POLYKARP KUSCH *was born in Blankenburg, Germany on 26th January, 1911 and moved to the United States at the age of one. He graduated from the Case Institute of Technology, Cleveland, Ohio in 1931 and gained his PhD in 1936 at the University of Illinois, Urbana.*

After one year at the University of Minnesota, Minneapolis he went in 1937 to Columbia University, New York, where he worked with Professor I. I. Rabi on the first radiofrequency atomic beam experiments, becoming a full professor in 1947. During the war years he carried out technical research into microwave generators at the Westinghouse, Columbia Radiation and Bell Telephone Laboratories before returning in 1946 to Columbia University as Professor of Physics. He has been chairman of this department from 1949–52 and again since 1960. For his discovery of the anomalous electron spin moment he received with Dr W. E. Lamb the Nobel Prize in 1955.

The knowledge of science and the power of a closely related technology have offered to man great opportunities for enriching life, for giving increased meaning to life. At the same time there can be no doubt that the opportunities have carried in their wake great problems and profound hazards. By some magic in the human spirit man has somehow or other managed to muddle through, and the human condition would be conceded, by a fair fraction of humanity to be better than it was a few centuries ago.

The opportunities are greater and the hazards are more portentous in this half of the present century than they have ever been before. This is a consequence of a very rapidly evolving body of scientific knowledge, a highly effective technology and, most importantly, a compelling and almost universal urge to translate the knowledge of science and the power of technology into some kind of action, whether social, political, economic, or military.

Perhaps the greatest opportunity and the greatest hazard are associated with the subject described by the title of the symposium. Quite incidental to man's newly found ability to exploit nuclear energy for military and peace-time purposes, it is now possible for the first time in human history to expose world populations, without their consent, to radiation capable of producing deleterious changes in hereditary material. On the other hand, the biologist has acquired such a detailed and profound knowledge of the nature and chemistry of the genetic process that the day may not be far removed when it will be possible to exercise a high measure of control over the genetic characteristics of both individuals and societies.

It would be foolish to hope that muddling through will chart a wise course in the terrain of opportunities, problems, and hazards. Ultimately the direction that we take must be determined by all men; I am far from persuaded that decisions must be made by the scientific community alone whose members have, in fact, a unique knowledge of the scientific content of our problems and a highly developed skill in dealing with the knowledge of the scientific content of our problems and a highly developed skill in dealing with the knowledge. Any decision or policy must be made through value judgments about a whole range of things as well as through an evaluation of the scientific knowledge that is relevant to the problem.

In the present conference an attempt is made, first of all, to explore various aspects of genetics as they effect or, in an uncertain future, purport to effect the destiny of man. Prior to the century, man did not do much to his physical environment that had a major effect on the process of genetic change. Please accept the statement as a general one, from an authentic nonprofessional in genetics. Obviously, genetic change has occurred through untold millennia in the natural environment. Professor Reed discusses this process of change.

With the discovery of X-rays by Roentgen and the isolation of radium by the Curies a new factor was introduced. Through specific activities of man the normal genetic process could be modified, at least for that minority of the population exposed to X-rays or the radiation from nuclear decay. The problem is now much greater, thanks to the bomb, the peace-time uses of nuclear energy, the prevalence of television, and a number of other features of contemporary life. I am on very uncertain grounds when I suggest that man has imposed on his environment a number of things other than radiation which may cause genetic change – the contaminants of the atmosphere and the temperature in which he lives as examples. Professor Glass, an authentic professional in these matters, undertakes a more precise discussion of the Effect of Changes in the Physical Environment on Genetic Change.

Some of my friends among biochemists and biologists have the cautious belief that it may become possible to tailor-make the genetic heritage of each individual by inducing change in the chemical structure of the basic genetic material. I am not competent to have an opinion and defer, with pleasure, to Dr Tatum who discusses the possibility of manipulating genetic change.

These three men are the qualified experts. It is not possible to make an intelligent judgment and contribute to the determination of a social course without understanding them. Their remarks deserve careful and concentrated thought. It is not possible to have been a University teacher of science for more than thirty years without having acquired a very great experience with those who close their minds to the possibility of understanding any part of natural science. Open your minds for once; what these men say may well determine the future of the race, may determine whether the most marvelous thing in all creation, the human spirit, will flourish.

Dr Shockley, as I, a physicist, discusses alternatives. He is, as I know from a long friendship with him, concerned with the human condition and its future. He brings to the discussion of Population Control or Eugenics the critical faculties of the professional physicist. Society, by the very existence of social classes, non-uniform economic status, varying levels of aspiration, varying beliefs about the purpose and meaning of life, has, perhaps inadvertently, effected a modification of its genetic composition. Has the inadvertent policy been a good one? What alternatives are possible? Bear in mind that Dr Shockley is critical and informed but that some of what he will say is descriptive of his personal sense of values, of his own view of the value of human life, of his own hopes for the future of man.

Nothing is more destructive of rational thought about science-related problems than the common belief that everything a scientist says is validated by the criteria of formal science.

We are all products of our personal history and that of our

society. The moral values of man are often embodied in and described by his religion. Evidently the value of any human action that potentially effects the nature of man himself cannot be appraised without recourse to the values which have guided, or purport to have guided, the actions of the individual and his society. Even those men who have become detached from any formally organized religious body or who no longer give even formal allegiance to a body of religious doctrine, are inextricably involved in a set of values with an origin in religions. Dr Ramsey explores the Moral and Religious Implications of Genetic Control. I ask you to use his discussion to nurture a sensitivity to the interaction of scientific knowledge with other facets of human thought.

The possible societies and the possible kinds of social organization that one might envisage were one able to control the genetic heritage of each individual stagger the imagination. Not all such societies would be viable and only very few, I think would yield to their members satisfying lives. It takes someone other than an amateur in these matters to consider the effect of genetic control on social organizations. What is the effect on society of an extreme diversity among men or that of a rather homogeneous population? Would men willingly concur in a policy that might somehow dilute the age-old pleasure in offspring in one's own image? I am reasonably certain that these are not the right questions, but they are questions that I ask myself. Dr Davis, then, discusses the Sociological Aspects of Genetic Control.

You should note, throughout the conference, the range of knowledge and of cultivated insights that are brought to bear on the problem under discussion. If we achieve nothing else here, we hope that you will come to believe that to become a truly effective member of society you must be much more than a learned physicist, an imaginative biologist, a dedicated clergyman, or an inquisitive student of social behavior.

SHELDON C. REED

The normal process of genetic change in a stable physical environment

DR SHELDON CLARK REED *is Professor of Zoology at the University of Minnesota and Director of its Institute for Human Genetics. He is a New Englander by birth, a native of Vermont where he was born in 1910. He graduated from Dartmouth College in 1932 with honors, and went on to Harvard for his Masters Degree in 1933 and Ph D in 1935. Then began his career as a teacher and as a geneticist; he lectured in Genetics for four years at McGill University, and then returned to Harvard as Associate Professor of Biology for two years before and two years after the war, during which he served in the Navy. Since 1947 he has been at the University of Minnesota, first as an associate then as a full Professor of Zoology and Director of the Dight Institute of Human Genetics. He is an author, investigator, and executive of numerous scientific societies.*

My assignment is to present the essence of the science of human genetics so that the subsequent speakers will not have to pause to explain the simple facts of heredity basic to their discussions. I will spare you the detailed didactic description which my hundreds of beginning genetics students have endured because those invited to this Symposium have had some previous acquaintance with genetics and realize that a dominant gene is not made of red chalk and the recessive of green. What I propose to do is to describe one or more examples of the most important genetic mechanisms in terms of reproductive fitness and eugenic significance.

Gregor Mendel demonstrated the behavior of dominant and recessive traits without ever having heard of a chromosome. He realized that each offspring receives half of its heredity from its father and the other half from its mother. He could see that heredity depended upon simple manipulations of pairs of traits and was thus a function of the number two. The recent recognition of human genetics as an important discipline has been due, in large part, to the impact of the beautiful pictures of human chromosomes which are a proof of the reality of the Mendelian laws of heredity in man.

Most every physician since 1900 has known that Huntington's chorea behaves as a Mendelian dominant trait. This means that one member of a pair of an affected person's chromosomes has the gene on it which disturbs the person's physiology in such a way that the person behaves in a psychotic fashion, decreases in intelligence and loses motor control of the muscles. The grimacing and spectacular muscular incoordinations resulted in the branding of the choreic as a witch in colonial days but the psychological disturbances due to this gene are more harmful to the patient than the muscular malfunctions.

The most interesting of the early papers on Huntington's chorea, to me, is Bulletin No. 17 of the Eugenics Record Office by C.B. Davenport and Elizabeth B. Muncey, M.D. This study was published in 1916. It traces the genealogies of the descendants of the original choreic patients who came to Long Island and to Massachusetts. There were about six of the original persons with Huntington's chorea who came during the seventeenth century and with their descendants accounted for the 962 choreics identified by Davenport and Muncey in 1916, either as living patients or ones for whom records of their disease had been preserved. It is quite clear that this dominant gene has had remarkable fitness even though the patient dies a horrible death. The reason for the spread of this deleterious gene is that it does not usually incapacitate the patient until after the child-bearing period is over. The Eugenics Record Office Bulletin includes a fascinating map which shows the migration of the dominant gene for Huntington's chorea from the east to the west coast with steps of one generation or more on the way.

It is important to remember that in past generations both choreic and normal persons could expect to have significantly more children than were necessary for mere self-replacement; this permitted a rapid spread of the gene for Huntington's chorea as the country grew. Furthermore, if the gene should have a disproportionately large representation in the lower socio-economic groups, we could expect it to have a higher frequency than would otherwise be the case because of the higher reproductive rates of the lower socio-economic groups. These considerations do not indicate that some day everyone will have Huntington's chorea, they merely suggest why the gene persists in some individual family lines for at least fifteen generations, as in Davenport's material, and why its frequency is far above the replacement value due to new mutations.

The frequency of the gene for Huntington's chorea in the Lower Peninsula of Michigan has been estimated by T.E. Reed and Chandler to be about one per 10000 persons. T.E. Reed and James Neel estimated the mutation rate for this gene to be about 5×10^{-6} mutations per locus per generation or five per million. This means that not more than one case in ten results from a new mutation while the other nine out of ten were transmitted from an affected parent in each case.

This gene for Huntington's chorea is rare in the population but it is of great interest as a direct challenge to practical eugenics. In counselling young persons who have a 50% risk of having this gene in each of their cells, I do not have the conviction to urge them to refrain from having any children. Instead, I equivocate and suggest that the risks are so great that they should expect to be satisfied with a small family. The reason for this, of course, is that half of these individuals will not have the genes for the disease and would not have any affected offspring. If we cannot bring ourselves to control this most insidious of genes, we need not expect society to attempt to control less terrifying traits.

The heredity of a dominant trait such as Huntington's chorea is simple. The patient passes the dominant gene to half his offspring who eventually develop the disease. The other half of the children receive the normal gene partner from the affected parent and as they got the normal gene only they will have only normal children. The genetic basis for Huntington's chorea is simple but we still have come to no decision as to how to prevent the transmission of this gene which every sensible person would consider to be an absolutely undesirable gene.

We must move on to the recessive type of inheritance. We remember that a person's chromosomes come in pairs, one member of each pair from the person's father and the other from his mother. If two genes at the same place on the chromosome pair are chemically different, one of them may produce a result that you can see, such as chorea, and is therefore considered to be a dominant gene. The other member of the gene pair may not give a visible effect and because it is not evident in the person, even though present, it is called a recessive. If two people marry who both carry the same recessive gene at the same geographic position on the chromosome, one quarter of their children would be expected to have this recessive gene on both members of their appropriate pair of chromosomes. When the recessive gene is present on both members of the chromosome pair its effects will no longer be concealed as it was in the carrier person but will express itself and result in a trait such as albinism. Half of the children of the carrier parents will be carriers also, while one-quarter of the children will not have the albino gene present on their chromosomes at all nor transmit it to future generations.

The albino child usually is produced by normal but carrier parents. While one out of four children from two carrier parents will be albinos, most marriages are between persons without the albino gene so that in Caucasian populations we find that only about one birth in 20000 is an albino. You may be astonished to learn that while only one person in 20000 is an albino, one person in every seventy is an unwitting carrier of the recessive gene for albinism. The picture is very different among some tribes of Indians of Central America and Southwestern United States where about one in 200 persons is an albino and one in eight is a carrier. The reader is referred to the paper of Keeler in 1964 and that of Woolf and Grant in 1962 for the details of the gene frequencies which are remarkably similar for the affected tribes in Panama and in Arizona.

We do not know why these Indian tribes differ so sharply from other Indians and Caucasians in their astonishingly high frequency of albinism. However, it is impossible to prevent me from speculating as follows:

(1) The Panama and Arizona Indians must have had some ancestors in common many centuries ago. Some one of these

'Founding Fathers' must have had a mutation to the gene for albinism which has been transmitted to his descendants, perhaps being lost in some lines of descent but becoming well established in others as a result of genetic drift. Genetic drift is the process by which a gene can get a foothold as a result of random sampling in numerically small populations. Even a deleterious gene such as albinism with a fitness of perhaps only 50% could conceivably become frequent as a result of genetic drift alone.

(2) It is fairly certain that metastases from skin cancers and failure to find mates because of the albinism itself cut the reproductive fitness of the albino very significantly. However, it is possible that the normal carrier of this particular gene for albinism may have a slight reproductive advantage over the normal person who is not a carrier. Woolf and Grant produced the arithmetic to show that if the reproductive success of the albino is only 50% of that of the normal carrier, and the success of the normal who is not a carrier is 96.2% of that of the carriers, then there would continue to be one albino in every 200 persons indefinitely. What we are saying is that if the normal carrier of the gene for albinism has a slight reproductive superiority over the non-carrier, the continuing production of albinos will be assured.

Presumably this is also the case for the albino gene in Caucasians where we must choose between an unreasonably high mutation rate or a small reproductive advantage of the carrier over the non-carrier in order to explain the frequency of this deleterious gene. The carrier of the albino gene in Causacian groups does not have as great a relative advantage as does the carrier in the Indian tribes. This may be related to the considerably greater identity of the chromosomes in the small inbred Indian tribes compared with the Caucasian populations. However, this is sufficient speculation about albinism for the moment.

A second recessive gene which I will bring to your attention is that for fibrocystic disease of the pancreas. I was among the first to show that this disease behaves as a good Mendelian recessive in 1949. With this disease, one can detect the carriers in some proportion of the cases, though not in all cases. Some carriers excrete in their sweat excessive amounts of chlorides, as do all the patients, and thus may be identified. Fibrocystic disease is present at birth or appears during the childhood years. It is an unusually pernicious disease because it keeps the child in the hospital about half of the time. The child was expected to die of the disease in the past but now he often survives as the result of improved and continuous medical management. Only the very wealthy could afford the tremendous expense involved, so that in almost all cases the cost is borne by society via Blue Cross or other community resources. The disease is also relatively frequent, being present in as many as one per thousand of Caucasian births. The financial burden for each case to society is so tremendous that it is legitimate to bring it to your attention. The damage from the psychological trauma to the family and patient is of even greater concern than the economic aspects of the trait.

Fibrocystic disease was selected as an illustration of a recessive trait because it is one of the few of eugenic interest where some of the carriers could be identified with certainty in premarital tests. I would suggest that the simplest version of the 'sweat test' be made available for all persons upon application for a marriage license. It is possible that two persons found to have abnormally high chloride values might decide not to marry. Legislation to this end does not seem very likely to appear, which indicates how little concern exists for the birthright of each child. Everyone is much concerned about the health of the forty whooping cranes which live in Louisiana during the winter, but few people give much thought to the eighty children who are born each year in Minnesota with fibrocystic disease, at least from the point of view of prevention of the disease. There is always intense interest in cures for diseases but not so much concern about their prevention.

We have spent, perhaps, too much time on the sharply defined Mendelian recessives and dominants which, fortunately, are rare traits. Our most frequent traits, such as height and intelligence, are different from the clearly Mendelian ones such as the blood groups. One can be completely lacking in antigen B of the blood groups and have excellent health; on the other hand, no one could exist with zero height and a person with an IQ of zero would not be conscious. Thus, frequent traits are not all or none propositions but are variable in expression and, when measured, produce a skewed curve or often a normal curve. These quantitatively variable traits must depend for their expression upon more than one pair of genes and therefore are said to be polygenic traits. The most valuable kind of polygenic trait which we possess is that of intelligence, as measured by tests of any kind. Intelligence is not a single characteristic and we cannot measure all of it. Nonetheless, we can talk about intelligence in general terms and the word means about the same thing to me as it does to you.

The clamor resulting from the nature-nurture misunderstanding seems to have obscured the obvious relationship between the evolution of the cerebral hemispheres and the basic intelligence of each species. The chimpanzee is smarter than the cat, and the cat is brighter than the canary. The differences in intelligence between these animals are primarily genetic and obviously multifactorial and polygenic. One can view the astonishing expansion in size and efficiency of the forebrain from the modest organs of our insectivorous-like ancestors to the really incredible mental equipment of *Homo sapiens*, man the wise.

Let us speculate about man's breeding structure during the major part of the evolution of his intelligence. It is the consensus that agriculture began to develop sometime around 8000 BC.

Man's survival and increase was greatly enhanced as a result. Previous to this time there could have been only hunting and food gathering groups with no established urban life. Each breeding group had to be relatively small with considerable inbreeding being inevitable. In such small groups, favorable new mutations for higher intelligence could have been established quickly and spread rapidly to other neighboring clans or tribes.

Presumably the evolution of higher intelligence, as distinguished from the lower intelligence of the apes, occurred during the last one million years or so, which would encompass about 35 000 generations, a little less than thirty years per generation.

Let us now face the baffling problem of the rate of evolution of higher intelligence. There were no IQ tests for cave men. However, there is little harm in assuming that our ancestors of 35 000 generations ago had an average IQ of at least 30, in present day terms. If we assume that the average intelligence evolved from an IQ of 30, equated to the present average of 100, there has been an increase of about 70 IQ points in about 35 000 generations. This is two one-thousandths of an IQ point for the average rate of change per generation. This figure is an absurdity, in a sense, in that it is not realistic to think of any average rate of change persisting for 35 000 generations. However, this extremely small rate of change, whatever it might be, does serve notice that even during the greatest spurts of man's evolution the largest change in any one generation must have been modest indeed, only some small fraction of an IQ point.

The world population has now reached three billion persons and it will take only fifteen years more to reach the fourth billion. It should be clear that no large genetic changes in the average intelligence of the people of the world are likely to occur in one generation. If striking fluctuations are reported, one should discount them to some extent. They are likely to result from bias due to the use of different psychological tests, different sampling methods, or other pitfalls rather than from fundamental environmental or genetic changes.

Let me present an excellent example of the ease with which scientists can be mistaken. One of the main concerns of the eugenics movement depended upon the peculiar misconception that the mentally retarded more than replace their numbers, while the most brilliant citizens fail to marry or have few children. If this were true, the average intelligence of the nation should be falling, and man would be losing the trait which makes him intellectually superior to all other species.

The basis for the eugenic concern was the well established fact that the larger the family of children, the lower the average intelligence of those children. One investigator had calculated that the intelligence of one area of England was dropping by about four IQ points per generation. This could not continue for long without ensuing disaster if it were true. It occurred to me in 1949 that the eugenic premise might be based on a seriously faulty design of the experimental method employed. All members of each generation with no children had been omitted from the studies of the past, which might lead to a large enough bias to vitiate the possible significance of the negative correlation between the number of children in the family and their average intelligence. My very helpful wife, Dr Elizabeth Reed, and later a graduate student, James V. Higgins, and I set out to explore the problem. We found that it made a striking difference when the childless members of each generation were included.

Our study profited from an extensive earlier project at the State School and Hospital for the Retarded at Faribault, Minnesota. The 1911 to 1918 work was an evaluation of the intelligence and social characteristics of about 500 patients and their relatives. We excluded some of the family groups because the patient was not actually retarded or because he was epileptic. The 289 probands we retained seemed to be genuine cases of mental retardation without major complications other than those due to their retardation. We studied the grandparents and all of their descendants in these 289 kinships as well as the persons who married any of the descendants. This gave a population of 82 217 persons. The 289 probands were an insignificant fraction of this sample of humanity, which seemed to us to be practically identical with any 'random' sample of this size which might have been selected by any other means.

The results of interest here concern the 1016 families where an IQ value was available for both the father and the mother and at least one child; these amounted to a total of 4071 persons with known IQ values in this sub-sample. We are well aware that the value of a single intelligence quotient may be slight. However, in a large collection of IQ values the errors in the individual tests should largely cancel out. The sharp differences to be presented are certainly not the result of testing errors.

These data provided the expected negative correlation of —0.3 between the number of children in the family and their intelligence, similar to the findings of previous investigators. We found that the low average intelligence of the children in large families was anticipated by low average intelligence of their parents, as measured when the parents were children themselves. Thus, the future mothers of the 370 families each with two children had an average IQ of 104.5 while the future mothers of the five families of nine children averaged only 90. The intelligence quotients for both fathers and mothers showed a substantial negative correlation with the size of the families they produced some years later. This last point is very important and it had not been demonstrated quantitatively, before. It is also worth noting that the important and sharp drop in the intelligence of the parents occurred in those who produced six or more children. It is also significant that only 39 out of the 1016 families, or 3.8%, had six or more children.

This sounds as if the least intelligent were rapidly outbreeding the remainder of the population with the higher intelligence ratings. However, we have committed a gross statistical error by ignoring the fact that these parents had a sizable number of brothers and sisters who remained childless. Everyone in the parental generation must be included in the sample if it is to have any statistical validity. The previous workers had omitted one of the most important single classes of persons in the parental generation – the childless.

The necessary innovation of including the childless brothers and sisters of our parents results in a striking change in the picture. This is because there is an extremely important differential in intelligence between the childless and those with children. There is also a difference between the married and the unmarried in the population. This must be so because the severely mentally retarded seldom marry. The severely mentally retarded thus pull down the average of intelligence for all unmarried persons. This should not be interpreted as a reflection upon the intelligence of single persons, it is merely stating the obvious fact that the severely retarded are handicapped in obtaining mates, especially when they are institutionalized. The sharpness of this differential can be indicated by pointing out that 42% of our group of unmarried persons were retarded, while only 4% of the married persons had IQ values of 70 or below. The average IQ for the unmarried was only 80.46 while the IQ for the married was above 100.

Our findings have been confirmed by Bajema who studied the subsequent reproduction of a complete sample of children in the Kalamazoo Public School System.

The Minnesota and Michigan studies show clearly that if we take all the persons in one generation and arrange them according to their IQ values, then the average number of children for the persons with IQ values of 70 and below is only 2.09 while the average number of children for all persons with an IQ of 131 and above was 2.98. The retarded then produced only 2.09 children on the average when all of the childless ones were included, while all of the persons of 131 and above had 2.98 children. Thus, when the experimental design is correct, there is no excess of children produced by the mentally retarded. Indeed, the data which are given in detail in our forthcoming book, give some hope that the evolution of higher intelligence may be still continuing. It would be impossible to prove that there is any genetic change either for better or worse in intelligence because the rate of change for a single generation must be so terribly small in the world as a whole. So, while we cannot prove that the IQ is rising, we can show clearly that the eugenic fears of the past that the IQ was falling rapidly were based upon an error in experimental design and therefore without scientific basis.

Let us return to our central topic of the study of genetic changes in relatively stable physical environments. This subject is often called 'population genetics'. We have seen that the genes for Huntington's chorea and albinism persist for longer or shorter periods of time because these genes are transmitted from generation to generation with the need for only occasional new mutations to replace those lost because some of the affected persons failed to produce their quota of children. It is more important to know what is happening with a polygenic trait such as intelligence for many obvious reasons. Man has achieved his place as the species which has subdued all the others not because his muscles are more massive but because his brain is better. The record is clear that his intelligence has been improving at an extremely slow rate for millions of years. Presumably the genetic mechanisms for many of the small parts of intelligence are fundamentally the same as the mechanisms for Huntington's chorea and albinism. The greater complications are due to the fact that many more pairs of genes and many more environmental factors are interacting to produce the trait we call intelligence than is the case with a mental disease such as Huntington's chorea.

Perhaps the greatest boon resulting from the disciplines of evolution and population genetics is the realization that the orthoselection for higher intelligence is probably continuing today much as it has in the past. Are there any ways in which this extraordinarily slow process can be accelerated? Could we cause a more rapid increase in the proportion of genes for higher intelligence with the corresponding decrease in the proportion of genes for lower intelligence?

It is not necessary to accept any specific theory for the basis of intelligence to conclude that it can be improved. Those oriented toward the environmental philosophies expect improved education, the 'war on poverty', and other social actions to bring this about. All must agree that no large genetic change is likely to occur in the whole human species in one generation. The important question, from the practical point of view, is how to manipulate society so that the genetic gains and the environmental improvements will both be optimal. The aspirations of mankind are committed to this goal.

The practical problems of how to guide our evolution for physical and mental improvement during the many generations of the scientific future are of the greatest importance now. It is these problems that the succeeding speakers will struggle to resolve in their own way, as well as can be done at this stage of our knowledge.

BENTLEY GLASS

The effect of changes in the physical environment on genetic change

DR. H. BENTLEY GLASS *was born in China in 1906. He received his Ph D degree at Baylor University, Texas in 1932 and has been associated with several institutions since then. Since 1947 he has been Professor of Biology at Johns Hopkins University where he plays an important part in maintaining and strengthening the high traditions of that University in the biological sciences. A vigorous spokesman for American science, he is a member of the Board of Directors of the American Association for the Advancement Sciences and past president of the Zoological Section of that body. In 1958 he became a Doctor of Laws. He has been an outstanding proponent of the responsible use of science and his dedication to the integrity of the academic enterprise both scientific and otherwise is evidenced by his work with the American Association of University Professors of which he is a former President.*

It is not easy to appraise the effects of future changes in the physical environment of man upon his evolving genetic constitution. Much as we have learned within the past few decades about some of the parameters that must be measured in order to make any such estimate meaningful, there are far more at which we must still guess blindly. Nevertheless, it is possible today at least to state what problems must be solved and what information must become available to us before we can comprehend more exactly where we are going, in genetic terms, and how fast.

Evolution, for mankind or any other species, is constituted of changes in genetic make-up that provide better degrees of adaptation to the total environment. The physical environment is only a part of that total environment, and probably, except for setting the limits within life can exist at all, it is the less important part. Once life had conquered the physical environment, first in the waters of the earth and later on dry land, and once the organism had developed that amazing capacity which it now demonstrates to regulate its internal chemical affairs in spite of external fluctuations in the environment, adaptation took on a different aspect. Then it was that the presence of living predators in the environment and of swarms of parasites, the agents of disease, became of paramount importance. The evolutionary value of social organization proved itself, whether founded on instinct or on learned behavior. Man's intelligence, which we so fondly regard as the supreme product of organic evolution, is less a tool for coping with an inimical physical environment than one for regulating behavior in the context of the family, tribe, and nation.

If these generalities be true, it must follow that minor alterations of the physical environment are indeed unlikely to provoke any radical change in the human genotype. Only a cataclysmic alteration of human circumstances might be expected to do so. And yet, such is man that even the smallest modifications of our present genetic constitution in such essentially trivial aspects as skin color may strike us with consternation. We must therefore give the matter some consideration.

The ways in which the physical environment may affect the human genotype are two. First, the frequency of occurrence of mutations and of recombinations of existing varieties of genes may be altered. Secondly, the factors of the environment may impose new selective forces that alter the previous degrees of successful reproduction and transmission of particular genes, so that some are favored and others are gradually eliminated. Natural selection, which is a function of the total environment, thus alters the frequencies of competing alleles, that is, of the various chemical and structural states which it is possible for one gene to assume. The occurrence of changes in the physical environment may affect either or both of these components of evolution, which we may characterize as comprising two levels: the primary level of the raw material of the evolutionary process, the level of the origin of hereditary variations and of novelty; and the secondary level of the shaping of the genotype through the creative force of natural selection.

At the primary level of genetic variation, it is not necessary to devote much consideration to the place of recombination in the evolutionary process. This is not at all because recombination is unimportant, but simply because it is itself a secondary stage that must follow upon the origination of the genetic variations in the population, through the process of mutation. Recombination may enable each new mutant gene to be tried out in natural selection in company with a variety of modifiers, and so to find itself. No gene works alone in the complex control of metabolic and developmental processes. Each gene is thus known, eventually, by the company it keeps. Even so, the population must first be supplied with all the varieties of primary genes and their modifiers before recombination can take place; then, for the most part, recombination is genetically regulated in amount and is not broadly at the mercy of the environment; and thirdly the physical factors that do modify recombination produce much the same direction of change as they apply to mutation itself. That is to say, temperature changes and shocks, or ionizing radiations, in general increase the amount of recombination and thereby increase the amount of genetic variation at the disposal of the evolutionary process.

Physical agents that are known to be capable of producing mutations of individual genes or fractures and rearrangements of the chromosomes that bear the genes, and that at the same time are capable of penetrating the living barriers that rather effectively isolate the reproductive cells of human beings from external variation, include (1) ionizing, high-energy radiations, (2) high temperatures, and perhaps even cold shocks; and (3) certain chemical agents, particularly those that act strongly upon deoxyribose nucleic acid (or DNA), the hereditary material itself.

Analyses of the total range of detectable mutations produced by any of these physical agents in any of the experimental organisms subjected to experimental genetic analysis, from bacteriophages and bacteria to the higher plants and animals, agree without exception in showing that the majority of induced mutations are harmful. The exact proportion of mutations which are harmful varies with the species, but it is always preponderant; in fruitflies and mice it may comprise as high a proportion as 99 %, or even 99.9 %, of all mutations detected. It is not hard to see why this must in fact be so. At one level of analysis, the biochemical level, it is apparent that the usual effect of a mutation of any gene is to interfere with the formation of its primary protein product, an enzyme or a structural protein, or to cause a loss of its biological activity. In other words, mutations tend to block specific genetically controlled steps in metabolism. That is characteristically harmful. The broader level of consideration is that of the evolutionary process and the nature of its productions. Neither we humans nor any other organisms possess a large amount of useless chemical machinery. When any process, once useful, comes by some internal or external change to be no longer of use to its possessor, the inevitable occurrence of mutations will sooner or later remove it. This truth applies to useless structures, which become vestigial organs and eventually disappear. It applies also to physiological activities – thus the capacity to detect odors has diminished vastly since man's ancestors came to rely more and more upon visual stimuli in the guidance of his behavior. And it applies fully at the biochemical level, where we find that many substances so readily synthesized by bacterial and by green plants, such as amino acids, cannot be manufactured in our own cells, and that even some substances made by many animals not too distantly related to us we are forced to call vitamins and to seek in our food. Perhaps, if the food upon which man's ancestors characteristically subsisted in the past several million years had not regularly contained sufficient amounts of these substances, we today would have retained the capacity to synthesize them and so would not need them in our food. But here we are, with our synthetic and over-processed foods, and our vitamin pills in bottles!

The reason why most mutations are harmful is therefore a simple consequence of the fact that we have, over the ages, evolved to a particular state of adaptation toward our physical and biological environments. No, we are not perfect in our adaptations; but neither do we possess a superfluity of useless biochemical and anatomical lumber. This truism has an important corollary. Genes useful in novel ways can arise only from the genes that already exist in the species, and these are already engaged in performing specific vital functions. Merely to substitute the new 'useful' gene for an old gene serves no purpose. The new adaptation is lost in the swift and remorseless eradication of the mutant type despoiled of some vital function. Swift and easy is the descent to Avernus! The path to the light is slow and rugged! Geneticists therefore in general believe that really new beneficial genes rarely if ever arise by substitution. The process is more complicated. It is one in which an existing gene must first become duplicated so as to provide a dual locus, and then the evolution of one of these two duplicate genes can proceed in a new direction while the other continues to perform the vital function with which it is entrusted. Only in case the physical environment were to change so radically that genes once useful were no longer of any material consequence to the survival of the species would a supply of genetic material for a rapid evolutionary change in new directions become available at the appropriate time, and this situation seems most unlikely.

Evolution therefore cannot be speeded up in an adaptive direction simply by increasing the mutation rate. The harmful effects far outweigh the possibility of any benefit. If a beneficial mutation, in an altered environment, has a probability of occurring that is even 0.1 % among all mutations – and that value is probably far too high – 999 adverse mutations will be added to the population for each occurrence of the beneficial mutation. The physical and chemical agents that produce mutations are blind and undiscriminating. They produce mutations at all genetic loci that are capable of mutating and not merely at those that might provide some better adaptation. The important question to consider is therefore how great a total 'genetic load' of harmful mutations the population can bear, or under which it might succumb.

Every harmful gene that arises through mutation must be eliminated from the population through natural selection – that is, through the death or failure to reproduce of some possessor, else the frequency of the harmful gene will rise and the total genetic load will be increased. How may we understand this in specific terms? At the present time approximately four million births occur in the United States each year. Of these, a considerable number bear some tangible defect or possess an inner defect that later becomes evident. Perhaps half of these defectives owe the defect wholly or in part to some genetic cause. The best current estimate, which I have derived from data in the Report of the United Nations Scientific Committee on the Effects of Genetic Radiation (1958), is that about 4% of all births carry a genetic defect tangible then or later in life. Some of these are chromosome anomalies, such as the presence of a particular extra chromosome (mongoloid idiocy, Klinefelter's syndrome) or the lack of a particular chromosome in its normal double dose (Turner's syndrome). Thus disorders that affect intelligence and normal sexuality and that constitute several per cent of all inmates of mental institutions are of this nature. Translocations of portions of one chromosome to another, sometimes with comparable physical and mental effects, and probably always with an adverse effect upon the fertility of the bearer, have in recent years been found to be far more frequent in the human population than was ever dreamed. Besides the chromosomal abnormalities there are single or multiple gene effects, our inborn errors of metabolism and our structural defects. These include such representative defects of the gastrointestinal tract as polyposis of the colon, of the blood as hemophilia, of immunity mechanisms as agammaglobulinemia, of kidney function as phenylketonuria, of nervous and mental disorders as epilepsy and schizophrenia, of muscular and skeletal defects as muscular dystrophy, of endocrine disorders as diabetes and pituitary dwarfness, and of reproductive disorders that engender sterility.

These genetic defects are the fruit of the 'genetic load' of the population. In theory, there is a very simple relationship between the frequency of the genetic mutations that produce detrimental genes, and the equilibrium that exists between the influx of such mutations and their elimination by means of natural selection.

Doubling the mutation rate will upset the existing equilibrium. The load of detrimental mutant genes carried in the population will then rise until the frequency of defective persons is just double the original frequency. That is because natural selection can act only upon the individuals in which the effect of the mutant genes is expressed, and for influx to balance efflux a doubled mutation rate must be balanced by doubling the amount of elimination. Thus eventually, after the passage of perhaps twenty generations or more, a doubling of the mutation rate would increase the percentage of individuals with tangible genetic defects from 4% to 8%. In a population the size of our present population, that would signify an increase from 160 000 to 320 000 defective babies born every year. If our population continues to increase at its present rate, thus reaching the size of the present population of China with the next century, the increased number of defective babies would amount to 2 280 000 annually. This measure is our yardstick for evaluating the effects of any general increase in the mutation rate.

Of all mutagenic agents atomic radiations have been studied most intensively. These radiations include X-rays and the radiations from naturally occurring radioactive substances upon earth as well as the man-made products of nuclear fission and fusion reactions. There is background radiation in our normal physical environment, amounting to a gonadal (*i.e.* reproductive cell) dose of three to five roentgens in the duration of a single human generation of about thirty years. Approximately one-fourth of this radiation comes from cosmic rays, which vary considerably with altitude, since the earth's atmosphere effectively absorbs the radiation. At 15 000 feet, it is more than five times as great as it is at sea level. About one-half of the background radiation comes from rocks, soil, and building materials. The radiation from igneous rock is considerably greater than that from sedimentary rock, so that mountainous regions in general are more radioactive than coastal plains. Living in a stone house a person receives more radiation than in a brick house, and there is still less in a frame house. Finally, about one-fourth of the background radiation comes from radioactive substances, especially potassium-40, that are taken in with food and water and become internal emitters in the tissues of the body.

A vast body of genetic evidence supports the firm conclusion that the frequency of simple gene mutations and the frequency of single chromosome breaks each increase linearly with increase in dose of the radiation, and that there is no threshold below which mutations fail to be induced by radiation. My own experiments with the laboratory fruitfly, *Drosophila melanogaster*, have demonstrated that even a dose of five roentgens – no more than the human dose per generation from the physical background – increases the mutation rate as predicted. From this experiment, which was based on the detection of mutations in a total of 1 360 948 fruitflies, it may be calculated that a dose of sixty roentgens would double the number of mutations arising spontaneously, and that the background radiation accounts for less than one-thousandth of the spontaneous mutation. (The proportion would be greater in longer-lived species but even in man would be little above 5% of all spontaneous mutations.) This value is in good agreement with other estimates based on mutations induced by high-energy radiation in bacteria, flowering plants, and mice, ranging from thirty to eighty roentgens for the dose required to double the spontaneous rate of mutation, (see the Reports of the Committee on Genetic Effects, National Academy of Sciences – National Research Council, Summary Reports, The Biological Effects of Atomic Radiation 1956 and 1960). There is now also good evidence, from my own as well as other laboratories, that human and other primate and mammalian cells grown in culture and subjected to X-rays undergo chromosome fracture at doses of fifteen roentgens or less, with a frequency of 0.35 breaks per 100 cells per roentgen. Again, the relation of genetic effect to radiation dose is linear.

This conclusion means, in the plain language of the National Academy of Sciences committee, 'that any radiation dose, however small, can induce some mutations' and that 'the genetic harm is proportional to the total dose'. If this statement were exactly true, it would remain simply to judge the genetic damage done by every sort of exposure to nuclear radiations solely by estimating the cumulative dose received by the gonads from the time of conception to the end of the reproductive portion of life. Thus, from estimates that the population of the United States received on the average, in 1956, a cumulative thirty-year gonadal dose of three roentgens for medical and dental diagnostic purposes, one might say that this dose was approximately equal or slightly below the background radiation dose, and might increase the spontaneous mutation frequency by perhaps 5 %. Following the direction of attention to the undesirability of these exposures, much has been done during the subsequent years to reduce the dosage through limitations in the use of fluoroscopy, which supplied the heaviest diagnostic dosages, through the use of faster photographic films, through better coning of the X-ray beam and shielding of the patient, and many other measures. The total accumulated exposure over a thirty-year period may be scarcely at an average of two roentgens per person.

There are complications, however. During past six years, largely through experimental studies of mice exposed to radiation at the Oak Ridge National Laboratory, it has been discovered that although the quality of the radiations makes little difference, the rate at which they are administered is of great importance. A low dose rate, administered over a prolonged period of time, produces far fewer mutations than the very same total dose administered at a high dose rate, for example, within a few seconds. Thus, in experiments in which Chinese hamster corneal cells were treated in my own laboratory by J. Grant Brewen with doses of 50 and 100 roentgens at dose rates of 600 r per minute, 60 r per minute, and 2 r per minute, the number of chromosome breaks produced was scarcely one-third as great at the lowest dose rate as at the highest dose rate; and the intermediate dose rate yielded chromosome breaks exactly midway between the two others. Recent experiments by Brewen show that the difference is attributable to a repair mechanism that can operate when the radiation is received slowly but not when it is administered rapidly. We must, therefore, from now on reckon with dose rates as important parameters, as well as the total doses received.

Medical uses of X-rays and of the gamma rays from radium, whether for diagnostic or therapeutic reasons, are characteristically at high dose rates and consequently do the greatest amount of biological damage. Background radiation, and likewise the direct radiation from fallout derived from weapons testing, are on the other hand delivered at low – often very low – dose rates, and may be expected to produce fewer mutations than would be estimated from the magnitude of the delivered dose. Radioactive isotopes, whether natural (e.g. potassium-40) or artificial (*e.g.* strontium-90, cesium-137, and iodine-141), involve still another complication. Some of them become generally distributed throughout the tissues of the body, for example, cesium-137. Others become highly localized in particular organs. Thus strontium-90 becomes almost wholly located in the bones and cartilages of the body, especially the former, where the radiation may cause extensive somatic damage and evoke malignancy, but where the short-range beta rays emitted cannot reach the reproductive organs of the human body. Similarly, iodine-141 becomes localized almost completely in the thyroid gland, and may do severe damage to the organ; but the genetic effects of these two isotopes will be slight indeed. Carbon-14, an isotope that is both natural and artificial, represents a special case. Not only is it dispersed throughout the body, it is extensively incorporated into the DNA of the chromosomes themselves, both in somatic cells and in the reproductive cells. Thus while cesium-137 is not involved in the normal metabolism of the body and is quite rapidly eliminated, carbon-14, with a physical half-life of over a thousand years, is a highly persistent genetic hazard. Whenever a carbon-14 atom has been incorporated into the DNA of the reproductive cells, the 'semi-conservative' replication of the DNA molecule will guarantee that some descendant cell will retain the atom until the time of its disintegration, when a mutation will almost certainly be the final consequence. It has been estimated that the total genetic dose received from carbon-14 is thus about equal to that from cesium-137, although the dose from carbon-14 will be spread over many more generations after the exposure to fallout.

Delayed fallout, occurring on a continental, hemispheric, or worldwide basis after nuclear weapons testing, is of course at a low dose rate, far below the 0.2 to 0.8 roentgens per minute which W. L. Russell has found, at the Oak Ridge National Laboratory, to be those levels at which the reduction of mutation by a low dose rate reaches a maximum. The total estimated fallout dose to the reproductive organs of persons in the United States from nuclear weapons exploded through 1958 has been estimated (AEC, *The Effects of Nuclear Weapons*, 1962) to be approximately 0.75 roentgens. The total explosive force of the bombs tested through 1963 is 511 megatons, 100% fission, whereas 173.8 megatons (53% fission) were exploded through 1958. The thirty-year gonadal dose from delayed fallout from weapons testing to date is therefore probably about 0.225 r. If we divide this estimate by at least three to allow for the fact that exposure will be at a low dose rate, it appears that the increase in the mutation frequency will amount to the equivalent of about 0.075 r administered at a high dose rate, as when ordinary X-rays are used. It would follow that the fallout from past tests is producing about one eight hundredth as many mutations as occur spontaneously per generation. This would produce a small but not insignificant increase in the genetic load.

Nuclear war, should it envelop us, would be an altogether different matter. The populations of the combatant, or target, nations in a nuclear war would receive not only the delayed fallout from the exploding atomic and hydrogen bombs, but would also receive a very large amount of local fallout, at a high dose rate. Fallout shelters, strong and relatively expensive, can be constructed to provide a hundredfold reduction in the fallout intensity, a reduction sufficient to lower the first-day dose to less than 100 roentgens. While some portion of this remaining exposure would be at a high dose rate, the average for even the first day would be at a low dose rate. Assume a nuclear war of modest proportions, in relation to the size of the present stockpiles of weapons on both sides – a 20000 MT exchange, of which half might fall on the United States, and of which roughly half is fission and half fusion. It has been estimated by experts that such an attack on a protected population might leave as many as fifty million survivors in the United States, of whom half would probably be severely injured. The hale survivors would be forced into exposure to radiation outside of their shelters, at least after the first month. It seems doubtful that any survivor would accumulate less than a total of 200 to 300 roentgens, equivalent to about 100 roentgens at a high dose rate. For further details about the consequences of such a nuclear war, I must refer you to my paper, *The Biology of Nuclear War*, since time does not permit a full discussion on this occasion. We are concerned at the moment only with the problem of estimating the genetic consequences of a probable exposure of 100 roentgens gonadal dose to the entire surviving population.

Clearly, the effect would be enormous, more than doubling the spontaneous mutation rate. Genetically defective births would increase steadily for some generations, mounting toward a maximum level of about 10% of all births. Nevertheless, and strictly from the genetic point of view, I do not foresee that such an increase could bring about an actual extinction of the population. Experimental populations of fruitflies, mice, dogs, and pigs have been exposed to such doses in repeated generations without such an outcome. However, natural selection might be sharply increased as our ethical sympathies for the unfortunate became blunted by sheer inability to cope with the problem of medical aid and rehabilitation.

It may be more important to consider the effects of delayed fallout on the people of the rest of the world in the event of an outbreak of nuclear war. Here one who looks at the problem without national sympathies may afford to be encouraging. The extrapolation from our knowledge of the fallout produced by past nuclear weapons tests involves simply a multiplication of the fallout through 1958 by two orders of magnitude or of the total to date by a factor of 40. Forty times 0.225 roentgens is 9 roentgens. Even if our estimates of past and present fallout are in considerable error, we can conclude that the nontarget countries in the same latitudes of the Northern Hemisphere (comparable since the basis of estimation is the present dose to the population of the United States) will be subjected to only a fractional increase in the spontaneous mutation rate – about a 15% increase. In the Southern Hemisphere, the increase would scarcely rise to half of that. Thus, although every geneticist agrees that any increase whatsoever in the overall mutation rate is undesirable and will have detrimental effects, and though every defective child is a cause of agonizing heartbreak, it is not scientifically correct to maintain that a nuclear war would necessarily lead to the genetic extinction of all human life on this planet, not even if the nuclear war were double or triple the size predicated, and even if most of the nations of the earth were actual targets.

Less horrifying is the problem of the risk, as we enter the age of nuclear power, of accidental exposures of the population to atomic radiations. There will of course always be a danger of accidents. Yet there is considerable reassurance in the monitoring of current operations, which show that nuclear power plants of modern types can be operated safely with very little or no contamination of the surroundings. On the other hand, there is accumulating evidence that radioactive pollution of ocean waters at the mouth of the Columbia River has been produced by supposedly 'safe' levels of radioactive wastes constantly leaving the great atomic energy plant at Hanford. There is little knowledge at the present time of the tolerance for radioactive contamination within different ecological habitats, marine, fresh-water, and terrestrial. Experiments conducted on underground nuclear explosions during the current partial weapons test ban have improved our understanding of the conditions that must be met to keep explosions from venting into the atmosphere, and before long it may be possible to use subterranean explosions for digging the new Atlantic-Pacific Canal in Central America. But much study must be devoted to the ecological effects of large subterranean radioactivity, and the drainage of underground waters must be carefully explored.

In one respect the inevitable nuclear accidents of the future are less alarming than the fallout from atmospheric weapons tests. The genetic damage done to a population is a compound function of the dose, dose rate, and number of functioning gametes treated, either when mature or in the ancestral germ line. For an acute dose, 1000 r administered to the reproductive cells of 100 persons is equivalent to 100 r administered to the reproductive cells of 1000 persons, to 10 r administered to 10000 persons, to 1 r administred to 100000 persons, or to 0.1 r administered to one million persons. For this reason, the fallout from weapons tests, which affects virtually every person in the entire world, is far more significant than the smallness of the individual dose from fallout would seem to imply; while the effects of a nuclear accident, even though doses might range up to several hundred roentgens for some persons, will be spread to far smaller numbers of persons, perhaps a few hundred or thousand only.

Temperature may be the most important single factor in the production of mutations in nature. Long ago it was established that in the fruitfly *Drosophila melanogaster* the frequency of lethal mutation is increased two and a half times by an increase in temperature from 20 to 30°C. Allowing for the fact that the length of a generation is about twice as long at the lower temperature, the actual increase per unit of time is five-fold for the ten degree rise. Mammals, with their internal gonads and well-regulated body temperature, might well seem to be exempt from such fluctuations in the mutation rate; and indeed, it may have been the importance of stabilizing the mutation rate, even more than the value of regulating general biochemical and physiological processes in the organism, that led to the evolution of a homeostatic regulation of body temperature. Yet our analysis must also reckon with the fact that in most species of mammals, including man, the testes of the male are slung in a pouch of skin, the scrotum, outside the abdominal cavity. Here they are certainly subject to temperature variation. In 1957 Lars Ehrenberg and his associates, in Stockholm, performed an amusing experiment. They undressed 25 young male volunteers and allowed time for adjustment to the ambient outdoor temperature. Another 25 young males, clad in their usual trousers, served as controls. The average temperature inside the scrotum, measured by thermocouple, was found to be 3.3°C higher in the males wearing trousers than in those who were nude. Here the evidence rests; but if we suppose that in the human species there is a relation of mutation rate to temperature comparable to that observed in *Drosophila*, the conclusion must surely follow that high temperature is a major cause of detrimental mutations. Perhaps our leaders of fashion, for both sexes, have not recognized the possibilities of capitalizing on this biological relation!

As for the chemical agents which are known to be capable of

producing mutations, most of them are rarely met with in the normal environment. Thus mustard gas or nitrogen mustard, formaldehyde, nitrous oxide, and ethyl urethane are not commonly met in ordinary life. However, certain carcinogens are also mutagens, and some of these may be found in smog. The common pesticides, now widespread contaminants in the environment of the United States, are also suspect and have not been adequately tested for their mutagenic power. Metabolically, sugars and ethyl alcohol are convertible to acetaldehyde, which like formaldehyde may possibly react with the DNA molecule and alter it – but then, possibly, there are barriers that prevent any access of acetaldehyde to the nucleus or perhaps there are enzymes which break it down so promptly that it cannot react in this way. The same possibilities arise with respect to molecular analogues of the purine and pyrimidine bases of DNA and RNA (ribose nucleic acid). Artificial analogues are among the most potent laboratory mutagenic agents known. What then of naturally occurring purines or pyrimidines? For instance, consider the case of caffeine, which is a potent mutagen for bacteria. Although caffeine has not been proved to produce mutations in any multicellular organism, a derivative, 8-ethoxycaffeine, is a strong mutagen and chromosome breaker. Perhaps our metabolic barriers keep caffeine out of the nuclei of cells; perhaps it enters but is not mutagenic; perhaps it produces mutations. We really do not know.

The effects of changes in the physical enviroment upon natural selection

Changes in the physical environment probably have a much greater impact upon the nature of selection than they do upon rates of mutation and recombination. Selection is the primary creative force in the evolutionary process. The varieties of genes produced by mutation are in their several combinations the raw material out of which the conformation of the species is carved. Selection is the force that carves the raw material.

Like a human sculptor, natural selection chips away the superfluous and the detrimental variants within the population. They either die before reproducing, or reproduce less prolifically than competing hereditary types. The population thus becomes more uniform than it otherwise might be. The individual and the species become suitably adapted to the physical and biological environment. Whatever change may occur in future in our own physical environment will therefore require some readaptation of the gentic structure of man, unless he can avoid this by insulating himself from the altered environment so as to maintain his own preferred circumstances with little or no change.

Man would be foolish, however, to suppose that he can avoid every change of circumstance that will have evolutionary consequences. Even now certain prevailing conditions are greatly changing the nature and magnitude of selection pressures. One of these is the decrease in the geographic isolation that formerly operated to establish and conserve the various human races and ethnic subgroups. A second is the steadily increasing size of populations. Both of these factors tend to homogenize the world's populations, although to say so by no means signifies that individual genetic differences will disappear. These will be conserved within the amalgamated populations, even though the differences between the groups will largely vanish. My own studies, conducted in part with C. C. Li, show the extent and rapidity with which this process is occurring in the present North American Negro population. This ethnic group, first brought to the New World a mere three and a half centuries ago, is now represented in our major cities by a population approximately 30% of whose genes are derived from White ancestry. The curve representing gene transfer from the White into the Negro population of the United States reveals interesting features. As time passes, the rate of genetic assimilation diminishes – the curve flattens out; so that at the present rate it may take 75 or more generations – or 2000 years or more – to reach a final equilibrium. But that prediction will be true only if the past rate of gene flow, which has been 2.5 to 3% per generation, is maintained. Social factors will surely predominate in altering the real outcome. Prejudice against mixed marriages may lessen; illegitimate births of mixed matings might increase; the very existence of a more mixed population may speed further intermixture. On the other hand, the establishment of a caste system such as India's conquerors imposed on that land long ago in their endeavor to maintain their superior status might prove quite effective in maintaining ethnic distinctions. The geneticist cannot predict the future. He can only study the dynamics of the processes now occurring.

The rapidly increasing size of earth's human populations likewise has inescapable genetic effects. Mating becomes more random with respect to most traits. Assortative mating diminishes, along with consanguineous marriages, and all recessive traits become – for a time – much rarer. In the population these genes will tend to increase under cover, and eventually having attained a much higher general frequency in the population, will produce homozygotes again, individuals upon whom natural selection may act. Yet for the time being, and presumably for as long as populations continue to grow, natural selection for or against the rarer recessive genetic traits is in abeyance. Thus if A and A' are two alleles, and A' is the rarer of the two, the population will consist mainly of persons who are AA or AA' and the $A'A'$ type will be absent. Only after the AA' heterozygotes become sufficiently abundant to stand a fair chance of mating, will the $A'A'$ type come back into existence.

In yet another way the growth and merging of human populations alters the nature of selection. It is only in quite small populations, of a few hundred reproducing individuals, that chance factors in the establishment or extinction of competing genes play any significant role. In a past not so remote, prior to the advent of agriculture, most men were members of quite small hunting and gathering groups, and mating was predominantly limited to the tribe. Under those circumstances random genetic drift – that is, runs of luck – probably played a considerable role in determining the fates of competing genes. And if some few bold adventurers, male and female, departed into the unknown to establish a new tribe across the seas or mountains, so small a group could not possibly be representative of the group of origin in its full range of genetic variability. From a population with individuals of blood groups A, B, AB, and O perhaps only the commoner groups A and O might be represented among the founders of the new tribe. That is what seems to have happened in the origin of the American Indians from their Mongoloid ancestors, some 20000 years ago.

The foregoing causes are not the only ones operating to lessen the force of natural selection upon modern man. Selection may be subdivided into the two aspects of mortality and fertility. If a dominant genetic trait is to be passed on, its possessors must on the average reach the age of reproductive maturity and must on the average produce at least as many offspring as the possessors of the alternative trait. The principle is the same for recessive genes, but because these may be passed on by heterozygous persons who are carriers of the gene but do not manifest the trait, the process is very much slower. Our ethics promote mercy and our medicine and surgery preserve to the reproductive age numerous genetic types that in a more ruthless society and a more rigorous age would never have had children. Diabetes affords a conspicuous example, but there are many others. Simple defects of vision, such as uncomplicated myopia, may serve to make the point more sharply. In a primitive human society keen distance vision must have been a necessity. Probably only after agriculture and needlework or handcraft developed could a nearsighted man pull his weight in the social group. Infants with defects were commonly exposed to the elements, even in relatively modern societies. Then, less than a thousand years ago, spectacles were invented, and the gene that produces myopia was no longer selected against. Today nearly everyone wears spectacles. I do not know whether it is likely that in time the gene that produces myopia will become universal and its allele that permits 'normal' vision will become extinct. Perhaps not, unless persons with nearsighted vision are more fertile in reproduction than their competitors, or our present 'normal' vision is associated with some unsuspected less efficient quality. But it is apparent that once we have created an environment in which glasses are a necessity of existence, we cannot readily reverse the process. Diabetes is no great physical disability – at least it does not prevent reproduction or seem to impair fertility; but we have elected an environment in which insulin is abundant and available and we cannot turn the clock back. Thus our ethics and our medicine are reshaping our genetic nature. Whether we guide our evolution in the future consciously or not, it is quite clear that we are shaping it unconsciously in many ways.

The tremendous reduction in mortality during the early years of life which has been achieved by modern medicine and nutrition, by surgery and by antibiotics, leaves every genetic type with little advantage or disadvantage in respect to others. Our evolution in the past has certainly included much selection for resistance to various infectious diseases, such as malaria, cholera, smallpox, plague, tuberculosis and the like. Such selection is now largely in abeyance. Instead, however, there is abundant scope for selection to occur, as James F. Crow has demonstrated, on the basis of differences in fertility. While the human reproductive potential, clearly not less than eight children per mother, is realized in some groups, reproduction is scarcely at the replacement level in other populations. Selection will favor those genotypes that produce the most children, no matter what their other characteristics may be. What I have just described is the biggest shift in the nature of human evolution that has ever occurred, and it is occurring just now. The shift may not, however, be very prolonged, since the prospective stabilization of the world's population within a century or so should have the effect of greatly reducing any selection based on fertility differences. If every couple were to reproduce at a replacement level, there would be no selection for fertility differences at all.

The elimination of selection based on mortality and also that based on fertility might leave *Homo sapiens* in an evolutionary status quo, except for the continued loss of whatever hereditary characteristics are no longer vital to him (or her). We may speculate gloomily that there will be many dysgenic effects resulting from the physical degeneration of structures no longer necessary because our instrumentation and our sources of power and locomotion will have made them useless. Our bodies bear witness to the elimination of the superfluous. We have already lost the use of the muscles of our ears, and the rudimentary appendix, wisdom teeth, and the mere remnant of hair that crowns the head will not be with us long. Clothes and cooking have changed us a lot already. Dare we look a bit farther and envision a new race of humans who have vestigial legs, since they walk so little and ride so much? Without mammary glands, since cow's milk and artificial substitutes have replaced the need of lactation? Or even without intelligence comparable to ours, because thinking has been handed over to the computers? Will the Man of Tomorrow need to spend a large part of his day getting ready to face the world, putting on his spectacles and adjusting his hearing aid, inserting his teeth, adding his false hair, taking insulin shots in one arm and allergy shots in the other, and topping it off with a tranquilizer before venturing to step into his car? All these alterations of the human phenotype are hardly to be regarded as dysgenic if we can indefinitely maintain our social capacity to compensate for them, although the burden of social labor required for so unproductive an effort may be expected to increase constantly.

It seems unlikely that new paths of evolution will open before us without some strong *challenge* of our present adaptation to our environment. For example, any further evolution of higher intellectual competencies than we now possess will not be possible unless the future physical environment or future human practices lead to greater reproduction of the mentally well-endowed. Yet we cannot define the 'well-endowed' precisely, either on the basis of present genetic knowledge and methods of personality and intelligence testing, or without knowing prophetically the nature of that future environment in which mortals will dwell.

In general, biological evolution moves with glacial slowness. Man as a species may have originated more than a million years ago, according to the latest revisions of prehistory made by the anthropologists, and certainly man has not changed perceptibly in the past 40000 years, although that latest period has seen such vast physical changes as the diminution of the rigor of the Ice Ages, the advent of more abundant food supplies through the introduction of agriculture, the rapidly increasing command of inanimate sources of power, and all the complex growth of a civilization based upon scientific technology. The best evidence existing at present regarding the speed of genetic adaptation to a new environmental situation comes from the presence in many tropical and subtropical human populations of relatively high frequencies of genes, otherwise adverse, such as those for sickle hemoglobin, thalassemia, and glucose-6-phosphate dehydrogenase deficiency, for these genes seem to owe their local abundance to their capacity to confer some degree of resistance toward falciparum malaria. It is reasonable to believe that falciparum malaria, like plague, is a disease of civilized, agricultural mankind, since it exists only in cleared country and where populations are fairly dense. If so, malaria as a human endemic disease can scarcely date back more than eight or ten thousand years, and a significant change in human heredity, a change of an adaptive kind, must be able to occur within that span of time, approximately 300 to 400 human generations.

The Man and Woman of Tomorrow are not really likely to be the caricatures of the Man and Woman of Today I have previously sketched, unless we submit ourselves to the more extreme environments of the Moon or of Mars as dwelling-places. Even there we are more likely to carry our terrestrial environment, with all its conventional circumstances, along with us, than we are to adapt ourselves radically to novel conditions. Within a few decades, in all probability, it will be experimentally feasible to grow human spermatozoa and ova in the laboratory, to conduct selected fertilizations between desired types, and to implant the young embryos in the wombs of foster mothers, providing such can be found willing. Not only the selection of particular types, but also what we might call genetic surgery may become possible, by treating a germ cell defective in some gene with DNA known to be sound in that respect. I say *feasible* and *possible*. I do not say either advisable or wise. Within just a few years we must decide whether to permit such human reproductive engineering. Yet at present we do not comprehend our own genetic natures, we cannot distinguish the 'fit' or 'better' genotype from the 'worse', we do not agree upon our goals. Will it not be easier as well as wiser to select and shape the environment to which adaptation must be made than to change our own inmost nature for the better? I have, of course, but chosen another way of saying that our cultural evolution has outstripped our biological evolution, and is far more likely to dominate the future.

EDWARD L. TATUM

The possibility of manipululating genetic change

DR EDWARD L. TATUM, *co-winner of the Nobel Prize for Medicine and Physiology in 1958, was born at Boulder, Colorado in 1909. Dr Tatum did all of his academic work at the University of Wisconsin receiving the A B degree in chemistry in 1931, M S degree in microbiology in 1932 and the Ph D degree in biochemistry in 1934. He has served as a professor of the Rockefeller Institute, New York City, since January 1, 1957. Prior to that he had been a professor at Yale University and at Stanford University. Because of his outstanding research in the new field of biochemical genetics, he received the Remsen Award of the American Chemical Society in 1953. His special interests have been the nutrition and metabolism of insects and microorganisms and the biochemistry and genetics of micro-organisms. Dr Tatum is a member of the National Science Board of the National Science Foundation and of the Research Advisory Committee of the National Foundation.*

In discussing and evaluating the possibilities of manipulating man's genetic heritage, the responsibility assigned to me in this Symposium, it seems best to lay the foundations by defining what we mean and understand by 'genetic-heritage', and by 'manipulation'.

As often is true, we can focus on the definition of genetics best by asking further questions. What is a gene? How does a gene act? And how does a gene change or mutate? Before the advent of the new concepts and techniques of *Molecular Biology and Genetics*, the answers to these questions were available only in a gross operational sense. For example, a gene is the chromosomal unit of heredity which replicates itself precisely in cell division, and which is inherited by Mendelian laws; it determines a visible, distinguishable phenotypic character, and the gene is subject to random change or mutation, recognizable by a corresponding identifiable change in the resulting phenotype, or appearance and behavior, of the organism. Today we are able to enlarge upon these definitions in terms of molecules with specific chemical structures and biological functions. Thus, we can now speak of a gene as a molecule of DNA (deoxyribonucleic acid), composed of a double helix made up of two backbones of alternating sugar and phosphate units, to which are attached four different pyrimidine and purine bases. The individuality of each gene depends on the exact sequential order of bases along each single strand. The bases are arranged on the two intertwined strands of the double helix in a complementary order, such that adenine on one strand is held to thymine on the other, and guanine to cytosine, by hydrogen bonds, thus maintaining the double helix. We can visualise the essential genetic function of replication of each gene as an enzymatic process of assembly of two new daughter strands on the parental strands, each of which, through specific pairing of bases, serves as a template or pattern in the assembly process.

We have a clearer picture of gene action, with one strand of the DNA molecule serving similarly as a template for the enzymatic assembly of a complementary single stranded molecule of another type of nucleic acid, RNA (ribonucleic acid), which serves as a 'messenger' to carry the information coded in the base sequence of DNA from the nucleus of the cell to the cytoplasm. Here this information is read by the protein factories of the cell, the ribosomes, and transcribed by the assembly of activated amino acids into enzymes and other proteins. These enzymes are protein catalysts which have very specific jobs to do in the cell, and the total complex of enzymes of each cell determines all the complex properties and characteristics of that cell, *i.e.* its metabolism, function, and ultimately its appearance and behavior. Thus, the entire complex series of events involved in the translation of the genotype into phenotype is interpretable as the translation of DNA into protein by steps which we are coming to understand in greater and greater detail.

Similarly, at the molecular level, mutation is thought of as the replacement of one base in DNA by another base. By thus changing the triplet code symbol for one amino acid to another symbol for a second amino acid, the amino acid sequence in the final protein molecule is changed by one amino acid. Depending on the particular replacement and the importance of its position in the enzyme molecule, the enzyme activity of the product may be qualitatively altered, or may vary quantitatively from complete inactivity to normal or even to enhanced activity of the 'mutant' enzyme.

The development of these general concepts of molecular genetics has been due to several factors. One has been the extensive use of microrganisms, fungi, bacteria, and viruses, in attacking and clarifying the problems of gene nature replication, function, and mutation. Another factor has been the rapid increase in knowledge of the intimate structure of complex macromolecules such as nucleic acids and proteins. The third important factor has been the development of techniques of isolating these molecules and for studying their interrelationships, and their activities, in *in vitro* cell-free systems in a test tube in the laboratory. As examples we may mention: X-ray diffraction analysis of DNA led to the recognition of its helical structure; chromatographic techniques are making possible the determination of the precise amino acid sequence of enzymes; techniques for separating and reforming nucleic acid double helices are making it possible to detect base sequence similarities between two samples of DNA or between DNA and RNA, and to isolate and study 'messenger' RNA; finally, the development of cell-free systems capable of protein synthesis is making possible detailed study of the role of RNA in this process, with the consequent approaching solution of the 'amino acid code'.

For the purposes of this Symposium, however, more pertinent than the details of these accomplishments, is the emerging view that the principles of gene nature and action we have been outlining are in essence the same for all forms of life, from viruses to man, apparently including the amino acid code. Hence, we may fairly confidently predict that to the extent to which we learn how to manipulate genetic change in micro-organisms, we should in time be able to do so with higher, multicellular organisms, including man.

Let us therefore examine what might be meant by '*manipulation*' of genetic change. I would like to define 'manipulation' in a broad practical or operational sense, in terms of the experimental control or modification of the phenotypic expression of the genetic make-up of a cell or organism. Survival, selection and evolution of a species must operate primarily at the level of interaction of its phenotype with its environment. However, in exceptional instances the participation of an individual in the survival and evolution of his species may be decreased or prevented solely at the genetic level, as in genetic sterility.

Since, as we have seen, the long chain of reactions from genotype to phenotype runs from DNA to RNA to enzyme, and from the complex of enzymatic activities to ultimate phenotype, there are obviously many points of attack for control of the overall sequence. To the extent to which we can indeed control gene expression either by changing the genome (or genetic complex) of an organism, or by regulating its functioning, we will be 'manipulating' genetic heritage and change.

Let us clarify these possibilities by categorizing them as different classes of 'biological engineering'. We might call them 'eugenic engineering', 'genetic engineering', and 'euphenic engineering'.

'Eugenic engineering', or simply 'eugenics', would involve the selection and recombination of genes already existing in the 'gene pool' of a population. The effective application of 'eugenic engineering' would require the identification of desirable and undesirable forms or alleles of genes, and bringing them together in combinations advantageous or desirable both for the individual and for his species.

'Genetic engineering' I would define as the change of undesirable genes by a process of directed mutation.

Lastly, 'euphenic engineering', as the name implies, would be the designed modification or control of the expression of existing genes in an organism so as to lead to a correct, desirable phenotype.

It should be noted in regard to all three categories that their effective application would require not only the technical know-how, but also that the manipulator be able to recognise or design a desirable gene or combination of genes in terms of their effects on an organism in relation to its environment. As of now, we have only a limited technical know-how, and we are perhaps even further from the state of wisdom and insight needed to apply it advantageously if it were available.

Let us now examine each of these three classes of biological engineering more closely, with respect to the 'state of the art' in microorganisms, and the possibilities of their application to man.

Eugenics, as you know, is to be discussed by Dr Shockley, so that I will make only a few points at this time. One of these is to emphasize that recombination of desirable existing genes and elimination of harmful ones by selective breeding in any organism requires the ability to identify the presence of an undesired gene even when it is not obvious from the phenotype, as for a 'recessive' gene, in a diploid organism. In haploid microorganisms all genes show their effects in each individual. In certain heritable metabolic disorders in man, however, quantitative chemical tests are now available sensitive enough to distinguish an individual with two normal genes (homozygous normal) from one with one normal and one mutant gene (heterozygous normal). In such instances, eugenic counselling can already be applied effectively. Examples in this group are PKU (phenylketonuria) and galactosemia. These are both hereditary metabolic diseases in man which if untreated result in mental retardation. They are characterized by inability to metabolize the amino acid phenylalanine, and the sugar galactose respectively. Sensitive tests for detection of other 'hidden' mutant genes will undoubtedly be developed as biochemical knowledge of the basic effect of these genes becomes available.

Microorganisms, in contrast to man, have another important attribute, which applies not only to selective breeding and other techniques of gene recombination, but equally to the applicability of induced mutation or gene change. This attribute is a function of their size and simplicity, so that an astronomically large population of individual cells can be grown and examined easily and rapidly. Hence the microbial geneticist can afford to be satisfied if one bacterium out of a million is recovered with the sought-for genetic attributes, whether these result from a rare recombination of existing genes or from an equally rare mutation. Obviously, the situation is different with man!

In microorganisms, because of their unique attributes mentioned, several exceptional mechanisms of gene recombination have been discovered. One takes place through cell-to-cell contact, and passage of the bacterial chromosome from the F^+(male) cell to the F^-(female) cell. Subsequently gene reassortement takes place with daughter cell progeny receiving different combinations of the parental genes. This phenomenon was first observed at a recombination frequency of 1 in 10^8 cells in a mixture, but now with improved techniques and more fertile strains, can be as high as 1 in 10 cells.

Another type of gene transfer and recombination is the phenomenon of 'transformation'. This involves the transfer of genes in the form of DNA molecules in solution from one bacterial cell to another.

Thirdly, genic DNA can be transferred from one bacterial cell to another via incorporation into a bacterial virus. This process, called 'transduction', may be crudely compared to the transfer of the malaria parasite from one animal to another by a mosquito.

It seems rather unlikely that any of these processes can be applied directly to higher organisms and to man. Several considerations are involved in this conclusion. First is the relative infrequency of gene transfer by these methods, even in bacteria. Even if the efficiency could be raised to 100%, which is questionable in view of the multicellular structure of an organism such as man, there would still remain the problem that human somatic cells are diploid, having two representatives of each gene instead of one as do the haploid cells of most microorganisms. Gene transfer, to be completely effective, would have to involve the two genes in each cell. A saving consideration here, however, is that most gene mutations are recessive, and one normal or active gene per cell is enough to correct most mutant phenotypes. This is true for the simpler mutant metabolic disorders of man such as PKU and galactosemia.

In spite of these limitations to the applicability of microbial type gene transfers to man, they conceivably could be used indirectly, even with man. It is now possible to grow some types of human cells and animal cells in culture in the laboratory, and even to 'clone' them. By this is meant the isolation of a single cell and the growth of its progeny daughter cells to large numbers. Thus in essence, human cells can now be grown and experimented with just as can bacterial cells.

Studies of such human cell strains have shown that in some cases the cells retain the phenotypic (enzymatic) characters shown by the individual from whom they were derived. Thus, it seems feasible to attempt recombination and mutation studies with suitably 'marked' or identifiable strains, just as was done successfully with bacteria.

Already, encouraging results have been obtained. The formation of hybrid mammalian cells has been reported in mixed cultures, as detected by morphologically distinctive chromosomes as identifying 'markers'. Also the transfer of drug resistance characters of one mouse cell-line to another by DNA as in bacterial transformation has been reported from two laboratories. Transduction via a virus vector is currently receiving increased attention as significant in cancer production in animals by tumor viruses.

It thus seems not too fanciful to foresee the possibility of applying these bacterial techniques of gene transfer and recombination to human cells in culture. Even a rare recombinant cell could in theory be selected and grown to large numbers.

Similar considerations apply to the second class of 'biological engineering', 'genetic engineering', or mutation. Genes are known to undergo rare, random, 'spontaneous' change or mutation. The frequency of random mutation is increased by exposure of cells to physical and chemical agents or mutagens, as was first shown in 1924 by H.J. Muller for X-rays. It is also known that a gene can mutate both from the 'normal' to a 'mutant' state, and less frequently by 'reversion', from a 'mutant' to the 'normal'. Even this rare, random process of mutation could therefore in theory be applied to human cells in culture to change an undesirable gene to a more desirable form, if the rare cell with the desired form of the gene can be identified, selected, and grown.

In a more specific way, 'genetic engineering' by directed mutation can be foreseen as a possibility. In microorganisms we already are learning techniques of producing mutations in a non-random fashion, by the use of chemical mutagens such as nitrous acid and synthetic molecules related to the nucleic acid bases. These latter analogues are incorporated into DNA and upset the replication process so as to cause the replacement of the original natural base by another one – thus producing a mutation. With further knowledge and better mutagens, we can reasonably hope to increase the selectivity of mutation considerably.

Another potential future approach to directed mutation is via the synthesis in the laboratory of a desired molecule of DNA. This tailored molecule, or any desired DNA molecule if it can be isolated in pure state from an organism or cell, can probably be amplified by already known enzymatic replication processes to any needed quantity. This new or isolated gene can then hopefully be introduced into mammalian cells in culture, as in bacterial transformation.

If the rare desired transformed cell can be selected and cultured, the new cells so derived could conceivably be transplanted into a living organism, there to correct a defective function of the original host cells.

The problem of transplant rejection involved in such a process may be obviated by further progress in controlling the host immunological process responsible for rejection or by using the prospective host's own cells in culture for the transformation process. I think that the applicability of this general approach to human cells derived through any technique of gene transfer or recombination is obvious, and need not here be elaborated further. Thus, in an indirect, but theoretically feasible, way, we can foresee the future possibility of a purposeful manipulation of genetic change, even in man.

Finally, I want briefly to consider the third class of 'biological engineering', 'euphenic engineering'. I have defined this, as you may remember, as the control or regulation of gene expression, so as to alter the phenotype without genetic change.

It perhaps should be pointed out that genetic change in somatic, or non-germinal, cells of an organism may be considered as a type of 'euphenic engineering', in contrast to genetic change in germ cells. It should further be pointed out that development and differentiation from one cell to a complex organism most reasonably is now viewed as involving the regulation and control of gene expression by selective processes of gene activation and repression. Hence normal development may itself be considered as the prototype of euphenic engineering, with the developing organism itself as the engineer at the throttle and controlling the switches.

From this point of view, and considering that a great deal is already known about the regulation of gene activity and expression in microorganisms, the prospects of euphenic engineering in man seem perhaps the most immediate and promising of the three classes we have mentioned.

We now speak learnedly and impressively about endproduct feed-back metabolic control mechanisms, about gene induction and repression, and about operons and operator genes – genetic processes and structures concerned in turning microbial genes on and off. And we are beginning to recognize and study analogous processes in mammalian organisms and cells.

In a practical sense, it is gratifying and striking to realize that the simplest form of 'euphenic engineering' is already standard human therapy. This is the limitation of the production of an undesirable or harmful metabolite by dietary limitation of its source, as of the amino acid phenylalanine in phenylketonuria, or of galactose in galactosemia. It should also be pointed out that replacement of a missing or defective gene product also constitutes 'euphenic engineering'. Effectively used examples include substances readily carried in the blood, or missing normal blood constituents such as gamma globulin which is absent in the presence of certain mutant genes, or hormones such as insulin in diabetes or perhaps in the future, needed enzymes.

I have tried to present at least a birds-eye view of some possibilities for the experimental control and manipulation of genetic materials – which I have termed 'biological engineering'. I would hesitate to predict precisely when and to what degree the principles and techniques of the newer '*Molecular Biology and Genetics*' will be successfully applied to man. However, you will perhaps have gathered that I am optimistic that this will come, perhaps sooner than we anticipate, with the breaking of a few major technical barriers.

It behooves us then, as we are doing in this Symposium, while 'biological engineering' and the controlled manipulation of genetic change are still largely possibilities of the future, to devote some time and deliberate thought to the even more difficult question of how this knowledge is to be used wisely for the welfare of all mankind.

References

C. B. Anfinsen, *The Molecular Basis of Evolution*. New York: John Wiley & Sons, 1959.

H. Harris, *Human Biochemical Genetics*. Cambridge, England: Cambridge University Press, 1959.

R. D. Hotchkiss and E. Weiss, *Transformed Bacteria.* Sci. Amer., *195*, 1956, pp. 48–53.
F. Jacob and E. L. Wollman, *Sexuality and the Genetics of Bacteria.* New York: Academic Press, 1961.
T. M. Sonneborn, Editor. *The Control of Human Heredity and Evolution.* New York: Macmillan Co., 1965.
R. P. Wagner and H. K. Mitchell, *Genetics and Metabolism.* 2nd ed. New York: John Wiley & Sons, 1964.
N. D. Zinder, *Transduction in Bacteria.* Sci. Amer., *199*, 1958, pp. 38–43.

WILLIAM SHOCKLEY

Population control or eugenics

DR WILLIAM B. SHOCKLEY *was born in London of American parents in 1910. He was brought up in California, where he studied at the California Institute of Technology (BS 1932). He earned his PhD in 1936 at Massachusetts Institute of Technology. He joined Bell Telephone Laboratories in that year where he worked on the invention and development of the transistor. During the war he directed research for the Navy's Anti-Submarine Warfare Operations Research Group. Returning to Bell after the war, he directed the solid state physics research program which saw the development of the first transistor in 1948. In 1956 he received the Nobel Prize in Physics, jointly with two former Bell Laboratories Colleagues, John Bardeen and Walter Brattain, for their contribution to transistor physics. Dr Shockley is now Consultant to the Shockley Laboratory of Clevite Transistor, formerly a subsidiary of Beckman Instruments. In 1963 he was named the first Alexander M. Poniatoff Professor of Engineering Science at Stanford University.*

'Man will be nothing unless he has first understood that he must count on no one but himself; that he is alone, abandoned on earth in the midst of his infinite responsibilities, without help, with no other aim than the one he sets himself, with no other destiny than the one he forges for himself on this earth.' (From Sartre *Being and Nothingness*)

The concerns of a non-specialist

The subject *Genetics and the Future of Man* demands consideration by all responsible people. My personal active concern in this subject arose in considerable degree through specific observations. These personal experiences do not qualify me as an expert in the fields of genetics and sociology and my credentials are not of comparable standards with other speakers of this symposium. However, my views and thoughts are probably typical of many thoughtful people who are worried about these problems and for this reason may add perspective to the report of the Nobel Symposium.

The reality of the problem of over-population was thrust on my consciousness by a wartime experience in India. As a civilian scientist, I was assigned to work with radar bombing problems with the Army Air Corps B-29 Forces in India. The base at Karagpur was located about 100 miles west of Calcutta in the Bengal area in eastern India. I had a number of occasions to fly between Calcutta and Karagpur and each time I was struck by the monotony of the scenery. As far as the eye could reach from the low-flying transport airplane, I was surrounded by rice paddies which stretched out into a continuous plane, much like an ocean of grass. Occasionally, in this ocean, small islands in the form of clumps of trees arose. These trees represented villages of mud houses.

In these villages, the appearance of the thoroughfare was different from that in any American village. There was none of the customary rubbish or litter on the streets. A tin can, a bottle, or a newspaper was valuable to these people, and would be collected and put to use. Even the droppings of animals in the street were promptly picked up, flattened into cakes and stuck upon the walls of houses to dry, so that they could be used as fuel for fires.

There was no room for additional expansion as there is almost everywhere in our own America. There were no hillsides which could be terraced and put under cultivation and there were no forest regions which simply needed to be cleared. The only space left over was possibly the narrow mud dikes separating the irregularly-shaped rice paddies. A better geometrical pattern of these could, at most, provide 1 or 2% more cultivatable area.

In Calcutta itself the density of the people was depressing. Many appeared to sleep in the streets or in the shelter of doorways of buildings.

After I returned to the United States, I read a booklet[1] discussing the world population problem and in particular the availability of calories from agriculture. It pointed out that approximately seven calories of grain or its equivalent must be raised to feed an animal in order to produce one calory of meat for a person to eat. In America, we eat approximately half our calories as grain and half as meat, so for each calory that we eat, approximately four calories of grain equivalent must be produced. In other words, by going on an all-vegetable diet, our present agriculture could produce food for approximately four times as many people. In India and China, practically none of the food consumed is processed by animals. There is no slack in the

[1] Guy Irving Burd and Elmer Pendell, *Population Roads to Peace and War*, republished by Penguin Books: *Human Breeding and Survival*.

agriculture. Consequently, if there is a failure of crops in one year, the people cannot continue by living on animal flesh until a good crop returns.

On the basis of these ideas, I at first felt that I would not be in favor of sending food to relieve a famine in India. To do so would simply make the situation worse between that famine and the next. Until some way of controlling the population growth had been developed, it seemed to me that relieving a famine was worse than hopeless; it would even make progress more difficult in the future.

A few years after I had been through the reasoning I have just described, there was a famine in India; we had surplus wheat in this country, and our Government sent some to India. Did I write to my Congressman to object to this? No. At this time, I did not feel that my reasoning ability as to future developments was as sound as my feeling that we should not have our surplus food in storage while it could be used to relieve starvation.

I mention my own personal conclusion in regard to withholding help from an Indian famine in order to illustrate how difficult have been my own attempts to reach sound conclusions in respect to these difficult problems involving people.

I have similar difficulties in coming to clear views regarding qualitative aspects of humanity just as I have had with the quantitative aspects I have discussed. But I feel it is of importance to think about the problems and provoke dicussions so that wiser decisions can be made when it inevitably becomes necessary to make them.

For some years, I had wondered and worried in a general way about possible deterioration of the human race due to selective use of contraceptive devices by the more intelligent people who would then have smaller families. (Although this is an old worry, it is rarely discussed.[2]) Then a specific incident

[2] A draft copy of this chapter was furnished at the request of an outstanding newspaper science editor. He wrote, 'So far I'm having problems as to

brought my worries to sharper focus. A delicatessen proprietor in San Francisco was blinded a few years ago by an acid-thrower. The acid-thrower had been hired by an emotionally unstable individual who had a completely unjustified feeling of resentment toward the proprietor. To me, the impressive part of the story was the background of the teenager who threw the acid and blinded the proprietor. He was one of approximately a dozen illegitimate children of an irresponsible and destitute woman. This brought home to me the possibility that if we had a situation in which an irresponsible individual could produce offspring at a rate which might be four times greater than those of more responsible members of society, this was a form of evolution in reverse. It demonstrates a lack of elimination of the least fit, the opposite side of the coin of survival of the fittest, which has been the foundation of the evolution of the human race and other animals on earth.

When I started to prepare for the Symposium lecture, I attempted to gather relevant facts about human genetics. One of the most impressive stories involved a Dr X who came under consideration as a potential head for a new institute of human genetics. The man who told me the story had been in contact with Dr X briefly, between ten and twenty years ago. He had identified Dr X as a possible candidate because of Dr X's great interest in a disease closely related to Huntington's chorea, which Dr Reed has discussed in this Symposium. The disease that Dr X had studied had been imported to America by a family of immigrants three or four generations previously. Dr X had traced the genealogy of all of these immigrants and their descendants and had found that the disease was carried by a dominant gene which was not sex-linked. He had studied the entire genealogy of the family and had found that 50% of the children of some one afflicted with the disease would acquire

where it will be printed if at all. The opinion section of the Sunday paper thinks the subject is too hot to handle.'

the disease. This fact establishes the assumed genetic character. As for Huntington's chorea, the individual might reach the age of reproduction before the disease would strike and then a gradual deterioration lasting for one or two decades would set in, involving initially loss of muscular control and proceeding to helplessness and mental deterioration. The phrase 'a gruesome death' used by Dr Reed describes it well.

The man who told me the story described his recollections of how he had attended a meeting at which Dr X spoke. Dr X gave a thorough description of his research on the disease and how he had identified it. This was followed by some technical discussion and after this some one raised a new question. He said, 'Dr X, you have clearly identified this disease, and have shown its characteristics, but of what good is your work to humanity?'

Dr X was remembered to have replied that he was glad the question had been asked. He had talked to all of the people who might be carrying this disease. They had learned of its true nature. All who had a 50% chance of developing it had felt they did not wish to bring children into the world who would in turn have a 25% chance of having the dominant gene. All had been voluntarily sterilized. The spread of the disease had been stopped.

As Dr X descended from the platform, he had difficulty in walking. He held his legs in an awkward way. The man who told me this story turned to his friend who knew the candidate and said: 'Does Dr X's difficulty mean what I think it does? Is he a sufferer from the disease he has studied?' The friend replied, 'Yes he does, and he is fortunate to have been able to complete his important work on this disease before it was too late for him.'

I found real inspiration in this story of Dr X. I thought it would be one thing that my audience would always remember. It was a proof that at least in one case (*i.e.* an 'existence proof' in scientific vernacular) that the human spirit would overcome selfish, irrational personal motives so that 100% of a group of potentially genetically defective people would act in the interests of a better future for mankind.

Unhappily this existence proof was not founded on fact. Dr X actually *did not* stamp out the disease. He did not persuade other members of his family to become sterilized. There are now 70 descendants of his family, 35 of whom are statistically doomed to die a gruesome death.

These disconcerting refutations of the original story I learned from Dr Reed after arriving at Gustavus Adolphus for the Symposium. Dr Reed knew personally the details of this case of Marie's cerebellar ataxia. Dr X himself had been sterilized (this was probably the basis of my informant's recollection) and had earned an MD degree so that he could do research on his family's disease, but he did not succeed in imparting his principles to his relatives.

The experience of Dr X is consistent with that of Dr Reed as a genetic counselor. If the chance that a genetically defective offspring is 25% or less, then the parents will take the imprudent chance. (This Dr Ramsey has referred to as 'genetic imprudence' and evaluated as morally wrong.)

The story of Dr X is an existence proof of the need to apply human intelligence and human reason based on an objective, fact-finding approach to solve problems vital to the future of man. I believe that there are three chief threats that dim our hope of a bright future. All of these are the result of the shortcoming of man's ability to use his mind effectively to solve problems of his own creation. I consider that the three great threats man has created are:

(1) The threat of a nuclear war.

(2) The threat of famine, low standards of living and high death rates – all stemming from the population explosion.

(3) The threat of genetic deterioration of the human race through

lack of elimination of the least fit as the basis of continuing evolution.

All three of these threats have arisen from man's creation of the exponential explosions of technology: the first from that in atomic physics; the second from that in medical technology and death control; the third from the second and the explosion of the growth of technology of production which have lead to our abundant society.

All these problems have arisen from the power of the human mind. Can this same power solve them? Can men choose goals that can be reached without surviving the pains of any of these threats becoming a reality?

It is my conjecture that all of the speakers at this symposium do have a common set of values for goals desirable for the future of man. All would like to feel that the destiny which man must forge for himself on this earth, is one in which the human race will progress toward a richer, intellectual and artistic life for men better endowed by their genetic constitution to participate in it. To choose wisely those courses and to establish those sets of values which will contribute towards progressing along such a path calls for education and understanding spread widely throughout the human race. Two elementary but enormously important thinking tools directly applicable to these problems are the exponential explosion in man's affairs, and the nature of statistical probability for man's genetic structure. One of the chief objectives I have in preparing this contribution is to dramatize these two thinking tools with the hope this will increase their use in the thinking of the human race.

The exponential explosion

The concept of an exponential function is familiar in mathematics especially in relationship to compound interest and geometric series; however, in spite of its great importance, it is understood by relatively few people. An old fable, illustrated with figure 1 is the best means I have found to make it vivid.

A philosopher in an eastern country is supposed to have taught the ruler how to play chess. Out of gratitude, the ruler offered to give the philosopher some great reward and asked him to name it. The philospher said, 'Please, my family is poor, we would like to have some rice. Give me one grain of rice for the first square of the chessboard, two grains of rice for the second square, four grains for the third, eight for the fourth, and so on for all sixty-four squares, giving me for each following square twice as much rice as for the preceding square.' The ruler felt that the philospher had not asked for enough but the philosopher insisted, saying, 'If what I have asked for is not enough, may I then please ask for a greater reward after you have given me the rice?'

The philosopher was asking for the sum of sixty-four terms of a geometric series with the terms 1, 2, 4, 8, 16, 32, ... in which each successive term, corresponding to the grains of rice on a square of the chessboard, is twice as large as the preceding term and has twice as much rice. Figure 1 illustrates this situation; showing each grain of rice up to thirty-two grains on the sixth square of the chessboard. The figure has been drawn as if 1 000 grains of rice would completely cover one square, which will occur on the eleventh square after the original grain has been doubled ten times. After five more steps to the sixteenth square the rice will be deep enough to make a little cube with its faces the size of one square of the chessboard. In three steps more, the little cube will grow eight-fold and contain enough rice to make eight cubes which laid end-to-end will cover one row along the chessboard. The next three steps can produce eight rows so as to cover the whole board; and the next three steps will put such layers eight deep; thus in progressing nine steps from square sixteen to square twenty-five, the amount of rice increases from a one square cube to a cube the size of the chessboard. In about ten more steps a cube can be made ten times as long as each edge as the chessboard, and this corresponds

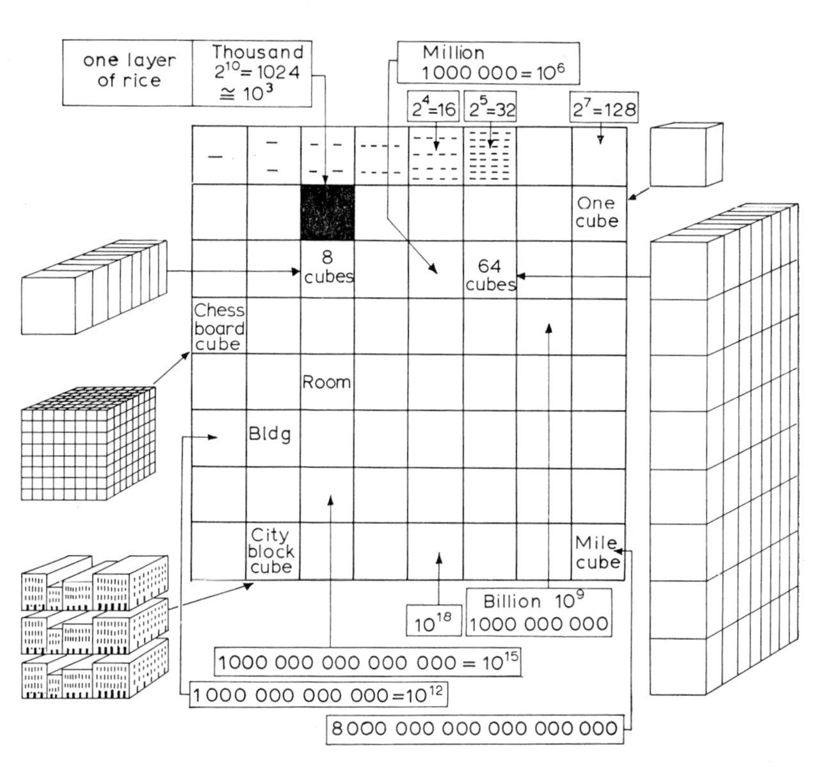

Figure 1. The exponential function as represented by the geometric series in the chess board fable

to the size of a room. In approximately seven more steps, about a hundred and twenty rooms can be made which is a fair sized building. And in another sixteen steps enough buildings can be put together to make a cube of rice about one city block long on an edge. And in the last five steps of the chessboard, this cube will become a cube one mile on an edge. This cube would contain enough rice to feed the entire present world population for several years. (The philosopher had asked for plenty!)

Anything which increases by a constant factor or multiple in each step is an *exponential function* of the number of steps. Compound interest in a bank is such an exponential function of the number of years in the savings account. The present rate of growth of world population is such an exponential function.

(exponents)

2 steps: $2^2 = 2 \times 2 = 4$

4 steps: $2^4 = 2 \times 2 \times 2 \times 2 = 2^2 \times 2^2 = 4 \times 4 = 16$

8 steps: $2^8 = 2^4 \times 2^4 = 16 \times 16 = 256$

10 steps: $2^{10} = 2^2 \times 2^8 = 4 \times 256 = 1000 + 2.4\%$

10 steps of 2 = 3 steps of 10 (plus 2.4%)

Figure 2. The meaning of the word exponent and exponential as illustrated by powers of two

Numbers which you write above and to the right of another number to mean that the lower number should be raised to that power are called 'exponents'. This is illustrated in figure 2, as well as in figure 1. A helpful and simplifying feature of making the calculations of figure 1 is the fact that ten steps of two is almost exactly the same as three steps of ten; on figure 1, I have neglected the 2.4% difference. This is brought out on the chessboard so that you can see that for every ten steps along the board the number of grains of rice is raised 1 000 fold over its value ten squares earlier.

At the present time, world population is increasing at about 2% per year. If this rate remained constant for 35 years, the population would increase by 70% if it were not for an effect like compound interest which gives interest on previous accumulations of interest. As a result the growth of the 70% which is added is just enough to account for another 30% and the population will actually double in 35 years. It will increase by a factor of 10 in 116 years.

People who are acquainted with the nature of exponential functions are quick to perceive that a population growth rate of 2% per year is a ridiculous impossibility over a long period of time. This conclusion is so important that I shall treat it as an example of the type of rational reasoning which the human race must accomplish in one way or another if it is to avoid long-term catastrophe. We shall start with two premises:

PREMISE (1) – *The present population of the world is 3 billion – 3 000 000 000.*

PREMISE (2) – *The rate of population increase is 2% per year and this rate has held in the past and will hold in the future.*

From these two premises, we can derive some theorems which are quite untenable. This kind of reasoning is known as the method of '*reductio ad absurdum*'. When premises are shown to lead to an absurd conclusion, then one can conclude that something must be wrong with the premises. (In this case, the thing that is wrong, of course, is Premise (2). It is quite impossible that the world population could increase at 2% per year over an indefinite span of time.)

Starting with Premise (2) and the reasoning of figures 1 and 2, we can at once derive two theorems:

THEOREM (1) – *In 35 years, the population doubles.*

THEOREM (2) – *In 116 years, the population is multiplied by 10.*

From Theorems (1) and (2) and Premise (1), it is straightforward to prove Theorems (3) to (6):

THEOREM (3) – *895 AD or 1070 years ago, there were only two humans.*

(To go back from 3000000000 to two requires a little more than nine steps of ten-fold each. Each ten-fold step requires 116 years.)

THEOREM (4) – *2665 AD, or 700 years hence there will be one square foot per person on every continent.*

THEOREM (5) – *2895 AD, or 900 years hence there will be one square foot per person on Earth, Jupiter, Saturn, Venus and Mars.*

THEOREM (6) – *3665 AD, or 1600 years hence, the mass of the people will equal the mass of the earth.*

It is evident from Theorems (3) to (6) that something is wrong with the premises. Theorem (3) puts the Garden of Eden at 895 AD. The thing which is wrong is that the 2% population growth has not actually continued over a long period of time, nor can it continue into the distant future. Table 1 gives some idea of what has actually gone on. It shows rough estimates of average rates of growth that have extended over certain periods. At the present time it is 2% per year for the world, or 35 years to double. However, the average rate of increase from 1900 to 1950 AD, was less than half as much, and if we go back to earlier centuries and to prehistoric times it is seen that the rate of increase was extremely small indeed. This very rapid rate of the increase of the population is the cause of what is now so often referred to as the population explosion. Table 2 shows the rates of growth of the larger countries having populations greater than 80 million. We see that the rate of growth varies by a factor of more than three, being less than 1 % per year in Japan, and up to 3 % per year in Brazil.

Countries having serious difficulties in raising their standards

TABLE 1

Population explosion;[3] *long term average growth of human population on earth*

Percent per year	Doubling years	Time period
0.001	70 000	1 000 000 BC to 1965 AD
0.02	3 500	50 000 BC to 1965 AD
0.3	330	1650–1750 AD
0.9	76	1900–1950 AD
2.0	35	1965 AD

TABLE 2

Current growth rates for the seven largest nations (28 Dec. 1964)[4]

	Population in millions	Growth % per year	Double time (yrs)
Japan	97	0.9	76
USA	192	1.6	44
USSR	229	1.7	41
China	690	2.1	32
Pakistan	101	2.1	32
India	468	2.3	30
Brazil	80	3.0	23

[3] See Joseph Marion Jones, *Does Overpopulation Mean Poverty*. Center For International Economic Growth, Washington DC, 1962, page 13 for estimates from 1650. Prehistoric estimates are based on approximate population estimates of roughly a hundred thousand at these dates.

[4] Based on *World Population Data Sheet*, Population Reference Bureau, Washington DC, December, 1964.

of living due to high rates of population growth are shown in table 3. Their serious difficulties arise in large measure from the fact that when populations grow as rapidly as 2% per year or more, very large percentages of the population are children; the additional requirements for housing, clothing, schools and so on, cannot be met while the low rates of economic growth prevail.

TABLE 3

Underdeveloped nations with population explosions; growth rate greater than 3% per year – population above four million[5]

3.2 Guatemala	3.0 Morocco	3.0 Thailand
3.1 Mexico	3.3 S. Rhodesia	3.4 Vietnam (N)
3.0 Brazil	3.3 Upper Volta	3.7 Vietnam (S)
3.2 Ecuador	3.2 Syria	3.6 Taiwan
3.0 Peru	3.3 Malaysia	3.3 Korea
3.4 Venezuela	3.2 Philippines	

TABLE 4

Smaller population growth rates 0.4 to 0.8% per year 85–170 years to double[6]

0.5 Belgium	0.8 United Kingdom	0.6 Italy
0.8 Denmark	0.6 Austria	0.7 Portugal
0.8 Finland	0.7 Czechoslovakia	0.8 Spain
0.8 Norway	0.4 Hungary	
0.5 Sweden	0.8 Greece	

Some of the more civilized and advanced countries have succeeded in maintaining their rates at less than 1% per year, as has Japan. These are shown in table 4. Control of the population growth in a number of these has been accomplished both by the

[5] *World Population Data Sheet.*

[6] *Ibid.*

advance of utilization of contraceptive technology and also by legalized abortion. Statistics are available[7] for Denmark, Sweden, Czechoslovakia, Hungary and Japan, and these show that the number of legal abortions is quite comparable to the number of live births; being in fact about two-thirds in Japan and even somewhat larger at some times in Hungary. The laws are so phrased that an unmarried woman not wishing to have an illegitimate child can be treated in a regular hospital rather than being involved in illegal and criminal actions, as is the case in America.

Abortion under favorable conditions is quite safe. The actual risk of death from a legal abortion in these countries is substantially lower than that resulting from the complications of pregnancy under normal circumstances in this country. Figures available for 1959 show a mortality rate of 22 per 100000 for births in America, by far the lowest rate among major countries. The mortality rate for abortions in Czechoslovakia, Yugoslavia and Hungary are about four times less than this, due partly to the restriction of legal abortion to the first three months of pregnancy.

TABLE 5

Year of birth and life expectancy (average)[8]

1850	38.3 years
1890	42.5 years
1920	53.6 years
1940	60.8 years
1950	65.6 years
1960	67.3 years

[7] *Human Fertility and Population Problems*, Schenkman Publishing Co., Cambridge, Massachusetts, 1963. See Christopher Tietze, *Some Facts about Legal Abortion.*

[8] *Biological Science – Molecules to Man*, Biological Sciences Study Committee, Houghton Mifflier, 1963.

The cause of the world population explosion has been the technology explosion, particularly the explosion of death control due to the advances in medical technology.

Evidence for this explosion is clearly given in the variation of life expectancy from 1850 to 1960 in this country (table 5; the figures apply to white males born in the United States).

These increases in life expectancy are evidence of the death control that has resulted from developments following Pasteur's epoch making work which eliminated confusion about the spontaneous generation of life and laid a foundation for modern sanitation. The effect has been to cause a great discrepancy between birth rates and death rates in underdeveloped nations, where the death control has come relatively suddenly. For them the birth rate has remained high and with the death rate dropping the population growth has soared, as has been shown in table 3.

The technological developments in death control have been in keeping with other technological developments which characterize the exponential explosion of our technology. These appear in terms of standards of living also.

The best measure of true economic growth[9] that I have found is the measure of improved standards of living given by the increase in 'real wages'. Real wages may be described in a simplified form as follows: in 1890 an industrial laborer earned about 15 cents an hour, and eggs cost 20 cents a dozen, so that a laborer could buy 0.7 dozen eggs for an hour of wages. In 1957 the corresponding values were $2.00 an hour and 57 cents a dozen; consequently, in 1957 the laborer could buy 3.6 dozen eggs per hour, so that 'real egg-wages' went up by a factor of 5. Figure 3 represents real wages based on a far more representative cross-

[9] The material on real wages and economic growth is based on my article *Scientific Thinking and Problems of Growth* in *The Impact of Science*, University of California Printing Department, 1964. See also Stanley Lebergott, *Manpower in Economic Growth; the American Record Since 1800*, McGraw-Hill, 1964.

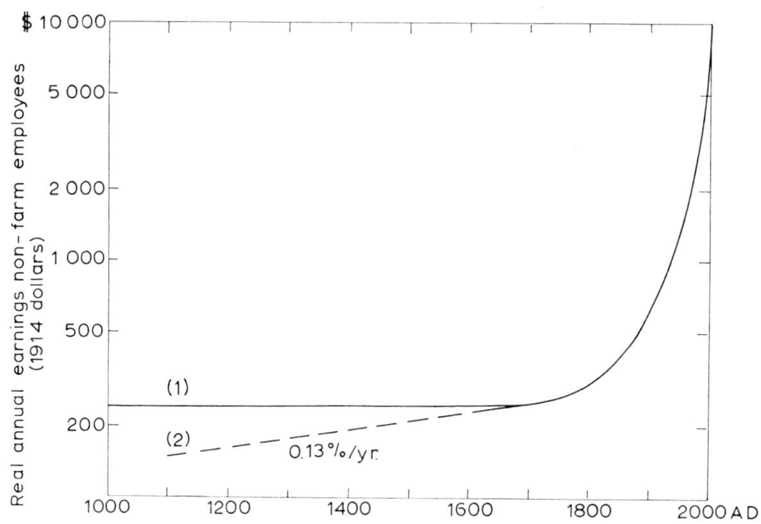

Figure 3. Real annual wages estimated back to approximately 1000 AD

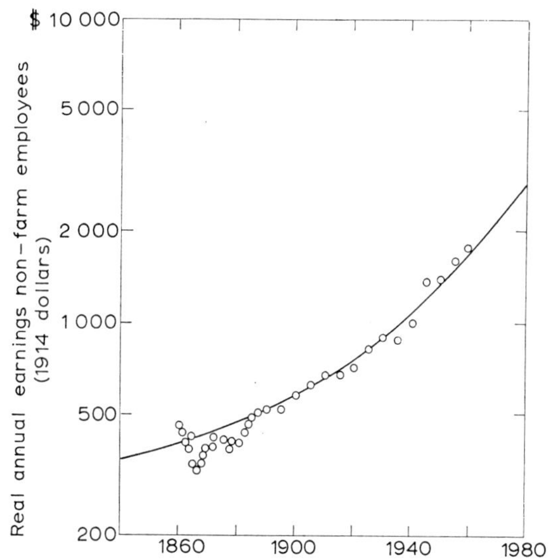

Figure 4. Real annual wages of 1940 dollars from Stanley Lebergott's *table (see footnote 9)*

section of items than simply dozens of eggs. The unit used is real wages in 1914 dollars, and a curve has been constructed on the basis of data obtained by Stanley Lebergott.

I shall discuss the part of the curve from 1860 to the present in more detail below, but first I should comment that the earlier part of the curve is based on a qualitative judgment together with the fact that it is hard to see how a laborer could have supported his family on an income of less than 150 1914 dollars per year. If this value corresponded to the year 1100 as shown on the chart, then the rate of increase of real wages in the middle ages was only 0.13% per year, so that approximately 500 years are required for real wages to double.

Figure 4 shows the actual data on which the curve of figure 3 was based. (This curve has been fitted by a simple analytic formula based on the concept of the 'engineer multiplier'.) The analytic curve of figure 4 is actually simply the 'exponential' function discussed in figure 1; however, the real wages values on figure 4 are actually themselves exponential functions of the rise of the curve on the figure. What this means is that the *rate of increase* of real wages *itself increases exponentially* so that the real wages themselves are the *exponential of an exponential.* To sum up, this is indeed a very rapidly increasing rate of growth.

What has produced such *striking increases of rate of increase* during the last century? Why, from 1100 to 1800, did real wages increase so little?

There can be little doubt in the minds of technologically competent analysts that the major cause of the growth of real wages is the *exploitation of basic science by engineers.* Further evidence that this is indeed the case is found by comparing the doubling time for the rate of growth of real wages, shown in figure 4, and the rate of growth of engineers in this country. It is found that the time of 49 years required for the fraction of the population with engineering training to double matches with a high degree of accuracy the years required to double the rate of increase of real wages in figure 4.

It can of course be argued that greatly increased production of trained engineers is only an effect rather than the chief cause of economic growth. In fact, some economists argue that the chief cause of economic growth is simply the accumulation of

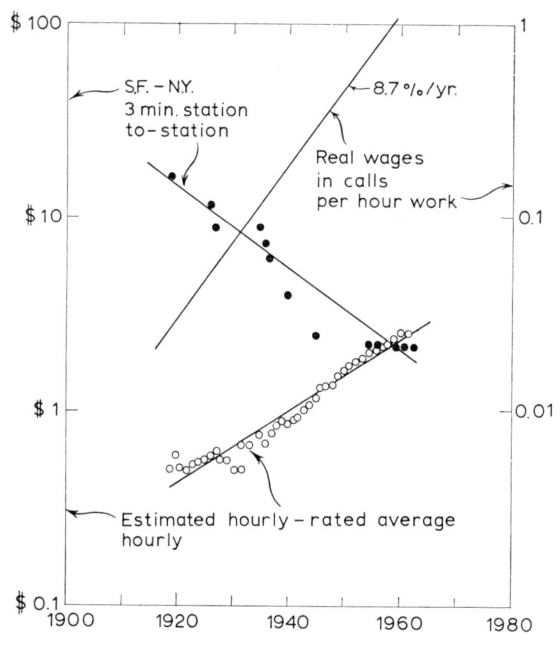

Figure 5. The growth of real wages as expressed in terms of long distance telephone calls

capital. This argument appears to me to be a ridiculously untenable view if one considers the flatness from about 1100 to 1700 shown in figure 3. It takes a fantastic naivety to assert that during these centuries the economic balance happened to be so perfect that the availability of capital investment remained so precisely balanced with depreciation over this long span of time that real wages changed only 0.13% per year, whereas now they are increasing at about 2% per year. Instead, I believe that the cause of the flatness was that there were simply no scientific discoveries and technological applications of sufficient importance to enable man's labors to be used more effectively to increase the items needed for his welfare; without technological inventions, like the steam engine, more capital could add little.

As a concrete example of the way in which real wages have increased because of technological progress, whereas they could not have increased significantly without it, let us consider real wages in terms of telephone calls. This is shown in figure 5. In this case two numbers are compared, the hourly earnings of 'hourly-rated' Western Electric workers who manufacture telephone equipment and the cost of a three-minute-trans-continental-station-to-station telephone call. It is seen that in about 1920 a worker could buy only 0.02 telephone calls per hour of work; in other words, a week's wages would be sufficient to buy only one such transcontinental telephone call. On the other hand, by 1960 he could buy more than one such telephone call per hour of work. There can be no doubt that this fifty-fold increase in real wages in terms of phone calls resulted from improved technology with reduced costs of telephone service. Without this improved technology capital investment could not have produced anything like the same effects.

Similar exponential explosions are to be found in the rapid increases in the scientific literature. In Professor Tatum's lecture he made reference to the 'compound interest' effect in pointing out that the rate of progress in genetics was increasing rapidly as more scientific developments were founded on all past scientific developments.

Prospects for population control and competitive exponentials

The exponential explosions depicted in figures 1 to 5 emphasize how rapidly have grown the rates of increase in percent per year of people, knowledge and things. So far as people are concerned, this is apparent in table 1 which shows that the doubling time for human population has decreased at least one hundred fold since about 50000 BC, when man had essentially his present genetic constitution. An even more rapid change has occurred in respect to the advance of technology and the increase in real wages shown in figures 3 and 4.

At the present time man's welfare is subject to the results of competition between several exponential explosions. If the population explosion proceeds faster than the economic and technological explosions, then certainly overcrowding, lower standards of living, and eventually increase in the death rate will occur. On the other hand, if the advance is rapid enough in technology and education, then the ability of the mind of man to deal with his problems may lead to keeping the population problems under control.

In any event, the exponential explosion of world population must inevitably be checked. Promise that man will find rational means to control the population explosion is given by recent[10] technological advances in practical methods for birth control. The most promising of these have come from improvements in modern plastics technology, as exemplified by the 'Lippes Loop' and other intra-uterine devices. Real hope that such a technological breakthrough will amount to an exponential growth of population control has been given by developments in Korea and Taiwan during a six-months period in 1964. At the beginning of this period practically no application of these devices was made. Applications have grown, however, in six months from

[10] Personal Communication from Dr. Sheldon Segal of Population Council, New York City.

nearly nothing to rates of about 80000 per year in each country as of September 1964.

Real encouragement that these rates will continue to grow so that the explosive growth of more than 3% per year in each of these countries will be checked is furnished by preference surveys. Interrogation of parents and potential parents in these countries, financed by the Population Council, showed that these parents wished to limit their families for very real and practical reasons. They will in this way be able to arise their personal standard of living by reducing expenses for non-supporting members of the family and at the same time be able to put their children into school and thus educate them better. These countries have seen the possibility of higher standards of living in economically developed countries through contacts with the West, and are eager to participate in their advantages.

The preference as shown in the survey by the Population Council is so strong and widespread, and the growth of the government-approved program is so rapid, that it is expected that within five years the explosive rate of population growth should be cut in half or less. It is evident that such control of population growth can enable the US Foreign Aid tax dollar to make real contributions to the economic growth of the country.

One of the reasons that the intra-uterine device represents a significant technical breakthrough is that it is extremely low cost and can be relatively easily applied. The skill required to apply it is typical of that which might be acquired by a high school graduate. Once installed, the Lippes Loop requires no attention and may remain in place for years.

About 15% of the women to whom it is applied cannot retain it. Whether this is a physiologic difference in women or whether it is simply that devices which fit properly have not yet been developed is not known.

Some religious questions may arise in connection with this

device. It may possibly work in either of two ways. In one case it may prevent fertilization of the ovum by hastening the passage of the ovum through the uterus. On the other hand it may hasten the passage of a fertilized ovum so that it does not become attached. In this latter case its role may be regarded as a form of abortion at a very early stage. Under these conditions it is possible there will be religious objections to its use.

In addition to plastic intra-uterine devices a battery of scientifically developed methods of birth control are needed, because cultural and religious differences prevent any one method from being everywhere accepted. On the other hand, the advances of medical technology which have led to the population explosion are for all practical purposes universally accepted.

The possibility of significant contributions to the welfare of the human race from research sponsored in this country are great and have been significantly increasing since 1959. It is interesting to look at statements which were regarded as being highly controversial in 1959. At that time the report issued by General W.H. Draper's committee had the following recommendation regarding the 'population question' in Latin America. The relevant paragraphs of the report read as follows:

'That in order to meet more effectively the problems of economic development, the United States:

(1) Assist those countries with which it is cooperating in the Economic Aid Programs, on request, in the formulation of their plans designed to deal with the problem of rapid population growth;

(2) Increase its assistance to local programs relating to maternal and child welfare in recognition of the immediate problem created by rapid population growth; and

(3) Strongly support studies and appropriate research as a part of its own mutual security program within the United States and elsewhere leading to the availability of relevant in-

formation in a form most useful to individual countries in the formulation of practical programs to meet the serious challenge posed by the rapidly expanding populations.'

It is hard to believe now that this relatively conservatively worded section produced in 1959 general consternation on a national scale, and provoked a government position that nothing could be 'more emphatically a subject that is not a proper political or governmental activity of function or responsibility'.

Since that time attention to the population explosion has been given by responsible individuals and organizations, and it has been discussed openly in the press. A significant step was the preparation by the National Academy of Sciences in April 1963 of a report entitled *The Growth of World Populations*.

The effects of these many efforts which have been given publicity by the press are seen in President Kennedy's forthright statement on population problems in the spring of 1963. More recently additional support was given in President Johnson's January 4, 1965, State of the Union Address:[11]

> 'I will seek new ways to use our knowledge to help deal with the explosion of world population and the growing scarcity of world resources.'

Many millions of dollars have been available at the National Institute of Health and the Agency for International Development to support basic and applied research on population control. Further evidence of public attitudes on these subjects is given by the Gallup Poll, which shows that since 1945 the percentage of the public that actually favor making birth control information available anywhere in the United States has risen

[11] On June 25, 1965 President Johnson said at the anniversary of the United Nations: 'Let us face the fact that less than $ 5 invested in birth control is worth $ 100 invested in economic growth.' In the 1966 State of the Union: 'To help countries trying to control population growth by increasing our research, and we will earmark funds to help their efforts.'

from 61% to 81%. At the same time those who are unfavorable have fallen from 23% to 11%.

Thoughtful people can draw great reassurance from the fact that these significant changes in public understanding and public attitude and response of the government have moved in such a direction that an existence proof now exists in Korea and Taiwan that this serious problem of the population explosion may really be solved.

As another example of *reductio ad absurdum* reasoning which is intended to interlock quantitative and qualitative thinking about genetic aspects of the human race, I would like to consider an alternative to controlling the population explosion by the means of birth control. In particular, I would like to show the difficulties which may be involved philosophically in trying to set up a condition in which we try to maximize happiness without at the same time limiting the number of people. Specifically, let us pursue one possible line of thought provoked by taking as a premise that 'our goal is the most happiness for the most'. Possibilities of both measuring and producing happiness by electrical instrumentation attached to the brain have been given by the experiments of James Olds with rats.[12] As the result of a series of experiments and developments, Olds found that if an electrode was appropriately implanted in the brain of a rat, and the rat was given a lever so that he could shock himself, the rat became so enamoured of doing this so as to receive the pleasurable effect of a shock that he would continue for 24 to 48 hours continuously, stopping only when physically exhausted. A rat which had previously learned the lever-pressing routine would ignore food despite hunger and indulge in a continued orgy of switch closing.

Let us now see how we may extrapolate from these observations to an imaginary situation producing the most happiness

[12] See D. E. Wooldrige, *The Machinery of the Brain*. McGraw-Hill, 1963.

for the most. We shall imagine that there are electrical means of measuring the responses in the happiness centers of the brain. We imagine that it has become possible to grow isolated brains *in vitro*, to attach electrical leads to these brains, which are being fed by a computer. The computer, in turn, can sense the response of the brain and electronically program stimuli to it so that the brain feels that it is leading an optimum life. This optimum life may, of course, be programmed to have periods of hardships as well as periods of happiness.

The brains *in vitro* system does not represent the logical end of this line of thought since if electrical circuitry can be developed, as seems almost certain now, so as to simulate the functioning of brains, then it should become possible to make miniaturized circuits which will be able to reproduce mental processes, including those associated with sensations of happiness, at even higher rates than can human brains. It would then be possible to replace all of the human brains growing *in vitro* by small computerized duplicates so as to achieve even greater experiences of happiness for larger numbers.

I consider this reasoning to be another form of *reductio-ad-absurdum*-argument: The premise that 'our goal is the most happiness for the most' leads to absurdities so far my own set of values is concerned. I therefore conclude that the premise is false.

I believe that most thinking people lean towards a set of values in which in the foreseeable future man will grow in competence by virtue of evolution. Man as a species is a genetically specified creature. I would like to think that evolution would develop this genetic specification to produce future men and women superior to us in all regards.

Is the competition between the exponential explosions now tending in this direction or the opposite?

Probability, genetics and eugenics

Many thoughtful people are now concerned about possible genetic deterioration due to selective multiplication of less gifted members of society through extremely large families or high rates of illegitimacy. Where survival of the fittest would have favored selection of only the best of these in past centuries, our abundant American society assures to all the privilege of reproducing their kind.

Evidence that human intelligence is largely genetically determined, although relatively scarce, is quite impressive. Especially convincing is that based on studies of the IQ of identical twins reared in different environments.[13] These studies show that such twins have IQ's that are far closer together than even those of brothers and sisters raised together in the same family.

Further evidence that intelligence may be determined by breeding has been shown by an experiment with mice. Mice were selected on the basis of their speed or slowness in learning their way through a maze. Fast and slow learners were bred separately. In nine generations two groups were produced; one was decidedly smart at learning mazes and the other decidedly dull.

As is well-known, intelligence, like many other attributes of animals, is not determined by a single gene, but is polygenic, so that its value is determined by the combined effect of many genes. The statistical consequences of this fact have led to a general reluctance of many people to believe, on the basis of their experience, that heredity is in any significant way involved in intelligence. When one discusses this subject with people not well educated in the field of genetics, then they often counter any approach to the problem of genetics and intelligence by mentioning cases which *appear* to disprove the role of genetics in intelligence:

[13] B. Berelson and G. Steiner, *Human Behavior*. Harcourt, Brace and World, New York, 1964.

For example, it is pointed out that Leonardo da Vinci was the only really outstanding offspring of a patrician family and that he was the bastard son of an affair with a humble village girl. I was recently told that many of the Australian families were the descendants of criminals of Cockney background who had been sent to Australia as convict labor and that the high quality of Australians today was contradictory evidence that character traits had significant genetic aspects.

In view of these contradictory instances, should one take the genetic determination of intelligence seriously? Can polygenic traits like intelligence and integrity and social responsibility even conceivably be beneficially influenced by eugenic approaches?

Some genetecists and many others withdraw from the idea that any deliberate control can be exerted in these subtle polygenetic traits. They do not usually consider a generally revered emotional trait that has so clearly been produced by eugenic means – the magnificent loyalty of man's best friend, the dog.

In thinking about these controversial problems, I believe it is useful to introduce a *simple model* for purposes of illustration. Although a simple model may not be entirely accurate, it may still have sufficient essence of the real situation to be helpful in thinking about the problem and in discussing it with people who are not well informed. Fundamental to these problems is the fact that an enormous variety of individuals might be produced as children of any particular man and woman. Since the human cell has 23 pairs of chromosomes, the normal course of fertilizing an egg means a random selection of chromosomes 23 times over. The most simplified estimate is as follows: for the first pair of chromosomes in the fertilized cell there are four choices as to the selection from the parents: two choices from the woman and two choices from the man. The same is true for the second pair of chromosomes. Consequently, so far as the first two pairs of chromosomes are concerned, there are sixteen possibilities. The number of choices, taking into account all of the chromosomes, can be considered by the same line of reasoning as that shown in figure 1. The possibilities introduced by each pair of chromosomes in the fertilized ovum multiplies the total number of possibilities as if one advanced two squares on the chessboard. In other words, the total number of possibilities that might result is the same as the number of grains of rice after 46 steps on the chessboard have been made. This means approximately 10^{13}, or about ten thousand billion possible offspring can result from making the random selection from the 23 pairs in the mother and the 23 pairs for the father.

For the purposes of the considerations here, it is not important whether the number of possibilities is 10^{13} or 10^{3} or 10^{60}. The important feature is this: the number of distinguishable different genetic blueprints that a man and a woman may produce is so great that any family they actually have represents only a tiny fraction of the possibilities. This conclusion is not affected by including considerations of duplication of genes from common ancestors which reduce the number of possibilities, or of 'crossover' effects which increase them.

Intelligence is polygenic and is thought to depend in some complex way on the combined effects of many genes in many chromosomes. Speculations about heredity and evolution can be understood in terms of an analogy that brings out the statistical features. The analogy I shall use is that of a poker hand from a stacked deck of cards or a part of a deck of cards. No individual card can dominate the value of the hand.

In terms of this analogy, *evolution works like stacking the deck of cards* from which the hands are dealt. Suppose after each game we threw out the cards in the lowest hand and went on to deal with what was left in the deck. Obviously, we would get better hands than before – but *only on the average* and *not necessarily* for any *particular* hand. Even if the rejection process went on long enough to reject all the low cards, say all the two's to sixes, for example, the stacked deck could produce 'no-pair' hands with the highest card a queen and *such hands* could be easily *beaten* by hands from an *unstacked* deck – but *the probabilities would favor the stacked deck.* This is the sort of effect that is supposed to occur for selected breeds of plants in animals that are not pure strains.

The *lack of obvious causality* in parent-children relationships can be represented in general terms with the poker hand analogy by treating each parent as a poker hand and dealing the child as five cards from the two hands combined. Suppose the parents' hands are each full-houses (for example, three aces and a pair of jacks, three kings and a pair of queens), the chance of dealing a full-house from the two hands is less than 5 % and hands as low as a pair of jacks and as high as three aces and two kings are possible. This model crudely represents two superior parents having a small probability of producing an equally superior child. On the other hand, consider parents represented by two low value hands each of which falls one card short of a flush in spades; combine these two hands and deal five cards, then 25 % of the time the result will be a flush in spades. This corresponds to the case in which surprisingly superior children may come from relatively unsuccessful parents. But neither of these examples invalidate the conclusion that the probability of producing good hands will be increased by discarding poor hands as a mechanism of stacking the deck.

Polygenetic traits such as human intelligence must almost certainly be represented by enormously complex statistical factors. I am not aware that anyone can even make a good guess about how many cards (or genes) are needed to make a poker hand that would resemble the complex corresponding to intelligence. However there is no reason to doubt that the genetic aspects of intelligence are governed by such probability laws. As for height and physical strength, intelligence is influenced greatly by environment. So far as intelligence is concerned, a typical estimate is that intelligence is determined 75 % by heredity, 21% by environment, and 4% by accidental factors.

From the point of view of evolution, it seems to me that the most important effect like rejecting the lowest hands to stack the deck can be described as '*extinction of the least fit*', rather than as '*survival of the fittest*'. This emphasis takes into account the fact that most mutations are unfavorable and many are lethal. Thus, they die out before the individual has reproduced. At the present time, the medical and economic exponential explosions that have produced our abundant American society assure to all the privilege of reproducing their kind, even though in many cases they may have genetic defects which would result in inability to survive to the stage of reproduction in a more primitive environment. This line of reasoning is one of the causes for concern of many thinking people about possible genetic deterioration of the human race.

To sum up, *there is no reason to doubt that genetic probability laws apply to human intellectual and emotional traits*. An elementary consideration of the probability aspect of the laws of genetics shows that the counter instances, like Leonardo da Vinci, are to be expected. The puzzling apparent contradictions that confuse many people are of the same nature as the surprising conclusions of probability theory. For example, the conclusion that if a fair coin has come up heads ten times in a row (which it should do on the average more than once in ten thousand tosses), then the chance that the next throw will be a head is still 50%. That Leonardo da Vinci appeared when he did does not prove the laws were not working. In fact the laws should predict a proper number of such remarkable cases.

The importance of lack of education and of social attitudes in regard to genetics and probability is shown by the story of Dr X and his inability to persuade members of his family that they should be sterilized and not take the risk of producing children who would with about a 25% probability be destined to die a gruesome death from the deterioration of their nervous systems.

It seems to me that general education on the reasoning given above on the wide variety of children who may be produced by one couple would help to overcome prejudices of individuals in regard to their special interest as parents that their own offspring should result from their own genetic structure. It is evident that what they will conceive represents only a small fraction of the possible results of dealing the genetic poker hand that picks by chance the blueprint of their child. It is even possible that some of the offspring that a couple might produce could have been produced by other members of their family, or even by quite other members of society around them. From the point of view of the long-term future of the human race they would often do much better with other genetic combinations than that particular chance combination that produces their own personal offspring.[14] Furthermore adopted and stepchildren are often very well adjusted and have as good relations with their 'parents' as do representative natural children.

All of these thoughts, I believe, produce feelings of uneasiness in people who think of them. I have found considerable uneasiness and discomfort in trying to think about this entire range of subject matter, and I suspect that most people who are not professionally in the field of human genetics or genetics in general, are similarly disconcerted and bothered by their own thought processes. I believe the difficulty is that we are forced to think of ourselves and other people as being not solely warm, living human beings with whom we can establish personal relationships, but as objects which can be thought of and dealt with statistically and analytically. My own reaction reminded

[14] Quite independently of my activities in this symposium, I have encountered first hand evidence that there exists an intelligent man who has independently reached this conclusion so definitely that he is actively seeking a sperm donor to improve the probable quality of his children. His wife shares his views. Their views are offensive to at least one eminent geneticist. They appear to be a very rare, perhaps unique, case.

me of a quotation expressing the same feelings in T.S. Eliot's *The Cocktail Party*.

> '...Nobody likes to be left with a mystery,
> but there's more to it than that. There's a loss
> of personality; or rather, you have lost touch
> with the person you thought you were. You no
> longer feel quite human. You're suddenly reduced
> to the status of an object – a living object,
> but no longer a person. It's always happening,
> because one is an object as well as a person.
> But we forget about it as quickly as we can.
> When you're dressed for a party and are going
> downstairs, with everything about you arranged
> to support you in the role you have chosen, then
> sometimes, when you come to the bottom step there
> is one more step than your feet expected and you
> come down with a jolt. Just for a moment you
> have the experience of being an object at the
> mercy of a malevolent staircase. Or, take a
> surgical operation.
> In consulation with the doctor and the surgeon,
> in going to bed in the nursing home,
> in talking to the matron, you are still the
> subject, the center of reality. But stretched
> on the table, you are a piece of furniture in
> a repair shop for those who surround you
> all there is of you is your body
> and the 'you' is withdrawn...'

I believe these uncomfortable feelings of being reduced to an object affect many people as they do me, when they try to think about problems of the future of the human race; for this reason most people avoid them and feel it is wrong to approach them in the sense of objective inquiry. Yet, it is of utmost long-range importance that enough people think about them with an objective, fact-finding approach so that a sensible concensus is reached. This will be specially true in the field of eugenics. As things are progressing now in which no steps are taken to discourage such genetic defects as diabetes and certain circulatory problems that can be corrected by surgery in infants, the genetic deterioration will continue. If this occurs, the biochemist and geneticist may develop additional means, like those available for diabetes, for patching up genetically defective offspring so that they may be successful citizens in a progressively more artificial environment. I believe this is a possibility which appeals to few thinking people. It does not appeal to me.

I believe that one of the most important contributions that I as a scientist can make to the dignity of man is to help him develop his objectivity and powers of rational reasoning so that he can face most constructively any idea that may confront him. With this thought in mind let me close this section by touching on some of the ideas of eugenics which raise problems that have by no means been solved but which a democratic society must, for its own preservation, consider.

If we consider not the mechanism of extinction of the least fit but the opposite of selecting the most fit, then we enter a realm of speculation which covers a wide range of possibilities. Since the time of Galton at the turn of the twentieth century, it has been proposed that the future evolution of man will involve his making these proper genetic selections from the most able and valuable people. One of the obvious difficulties is that it may be very difficult to reach agreement as to what does constitute the ideal type of man.[15] This would become extremely important if some of the more far-reaching proposals, like those of Muller,

[15] Footnote 14 furnishes a possible answer. The couple involved proposes to make their own decision as to a sperm donor based on all available information including interviews. This approach puts selection on an individual basis and eliminates the need for a universally accepted ideal type. The human race developed in the past on the basis of a multitude of such personal decisions (marriages for example).

were to be followed.[16] Muller proposes such things as growing germ cells of especially able men *in vitro* and using these for artificial insemination. Going even further, he proposes raising male germ cells and ova *in vitro*, accomplishing fertilization and raising offspring either *in vitro*, or by implantation into accepting foster mothers. In this way, individuals produced by genetic selection from especially able parents could become the foster children of wide numbers of people. Going still further, it has been proposed that the actual set of chromosomes from an unusually competent and gifted man might be surgically transferred from one cell to an ovum which would then grow so as to produce a twin of the exceptional man.

Muller's suggestions emphasize survival of the fittest versus elimination of the least fit. Such emphasis has foundation in theories of the evolution of man. Mayr in his book, *Animal Species and Evolution*[17] points out that polygyny (many wives) is more or less developed in all anthropoid apes and that there are good reasons for postulating that it was prevalent in primitive 'hominids' or precursors of modern man. This would give the leader of a group tremendous genetic leverage on the next generation. Leadership of successful tribes would call for intelligence, judgment and other attributes we admire in modern man. Mayr proposes this accounts for rapid growth of human brainsize during the last million years. Mayr analyses the present situation and concludes that in our society the superior person is punished by government in numerous ways, by taxes and otherwise, which make it more difficult for him to raise a large family. He suggests changing laws so as to make tax allowances for children a percentage of income rather than a fixed amount and making school tuition dependent on ability of the student

[16] *Man and his Future*, Little Brown & Co., Boston, 1963. See H. J. Muller, *Genetic Progress by Voluntarily Conducted Germical Choice.*

[17] Ernst Mayr, *Animal Species and Evolution.* Harvard University Press, Cambridge, 1963.

to learn rather than on ability of the family to pay. He states, 'I firmly believe that such positive measures would do far more toward the increase of desirable genes in the human gene pool than all the negative measures proposed by eugenicists of former generations.' He supports Muller's 'sperm bank' proposal.

A grim possibility for continuing man's evolution is the threat of enormous genetic damage from a nuclear war. Eugenics would then be forced upon the human race in much the same way as infanticide was in more primitive times, as a necessary step in the struggle for existence. Evidence that such a course might well be followed is to be found, to a very limited degree, in the aftermath of Hiroshima and Nagasaki. In Japan one of the largest studies of human genealogy and genetics has already been undertaken, as a concomitant of studying possible genetic damage produced by the atom bombs.

A challenging idea designed to fit into our profit-motivated society has been proposed by Kenneth Boulding in *The Meaning of the Twentieth Century*. I offer it as a provocative possibility worthy of discussion.

> 'I have only one positive suggestion to make, a proposal which now seems so farfetched that I find it creates only amusement when I propose it. I think in all seriousness, however, that a system of marketable licenses to have children is the only one which will combine the minimum of social control necessary to this problem with a maximum of individual liberty and ethical choice. Each girl on approaching maturity would be presented with a certificate which will entitle its owner to have, say, 2.2 children or whatever number would ensure a reproductive rate of one. The unit of these certificates might be the "deci-child", and accumulation of ten of these units by purchase, inheritance, or gift would permit a woman in maturity to have one legal child. We would then set up a market in these units in which the rich and the philoprogenitive would purchase them from the poor, the nuns, the maiden aunts, and so on.'

An example of an attitude in this country which seems to me cannot stand up under the light of any really logical and dispassionate considerations is the requirement for continuation of pregnancy by a woman who is either unmarried or has sound reason to believe she will produce a genetically defective infant, or one who has been damaged by unfortunate incidents during pregnancy, such as the effect of thalidomide. Such cases should surely have the opportunity to have a legal abortion in this country.[18]

To a limited degree, some understanding of the importance of human genetics has arisen in respect to sterilization laws for mental defectives. In a Supreme Court decision, Oliver Wendell Holmes presented a thoughtful appraisal of the difficulties in a majority opinion upholding the statutes for the sterilization of feeble-minded persons in the State of Virginia. Justice Holmes' opinion read, in part:

'...that Carrie Buck is the probable potential parent of socially inadequate offspring likewise afflicted; that she may be sexually sterilized without detriment to her general health; and that her welfare and that of society will be promoted by her sterilization... We have seen more than once that the public welfare may call upon the best citizens for their lives. It would be strange if we could not call upon those who already sap the strength of the State for these lesser sacrifices often not felt by those concerned, in order to prevent our being swamped with incompetents. It is better for all the world if instead of waiting to execute degenerate offspring for crime, or let them starve for their imbecility, society could prevent those who are manifestly unfit from continuing their kind... Three generations of imbeciles are enough.'

This furnishes an instance of an attempt to set up laws which will contribute toward replacing the cruel natural mechanisms of extinction of the least fit as the means of continuing evolution. Although laws for sterilization of mental defectives are on the

[18] A penetrating analysis of these questions has been presented in a reprint of a lecture at University of California, Berkeley, 29 April 1964. Garrett Hardin, *Abortion and Human Dignity*. (Available from: Society for Human Abortion, P.O. Box 1862, San Francisco, California 94101.)

books of many states, they are of questionable effectiveness. Furthermore, the majority of cases of mental retardation are not of genetic origin so that the genetic aspects are not relevant. Changes in California legislation and an institutional medical policy during 1951 brought about a sharp decrease in the number of sterilizations performed in the state hospitals for mentally retarded. As a result, participation has dropped from between 200 and 300 per year to a mere handful. To me one of the most serious aspects of all this is that public interest and awareness in these problems is generally nearly negligible. At least one outstandingly competent and humanitarian physician friend of mine was unaware of the changes in California, although his early medical experience had put him in first hand contact with the problems. Mayr's proposals of changing laws to favor large families of superior people represents another possible interaction between legislation and man's genetic future.

Lack of a national attitude supporting the objective, fact-finding approach in the field of human genetics is furnished by reports from government sources. Although census bureau studies have shown poverty and lack of education are passed on from generation to generation within families, research on genetic versus environmental aspects is apparently lacking.[19]

Secretary of Labor Wirtz is quoted as saying, 'There is a strong indication that a disproportionate number of unemployed come from large families, but we don't pursue evidence that would permit establishing this as a fact or evaluating its significance.'[20]

What is needed is a continuing objective, fact-finding approach to these enormously controversial, enormously signifi-

[19] See for example Sylvia Sidney, Financial pages, S.F. Chronicle, 2 December 1964.

[20] In reply to an inquiry of mine Secretary Wirtz wrote that he hoped this statement would encourage someone 'to ferret out the facts'. I know of no reason to believe this is now being done.

cant problems. I question if the great society or the dignity of man can really be achieved without it.[21]

One of the most difficult facts to face is that man is a mammal and subject to nature's biologic laws. In many states in this country citizens are denied the opportunity to learn this fact from the study of evolution; they cannot face with dignity exploratory thinking and research concerning the genetic future of man. I hold the following views: the general applicability of rational reasoning is inadequately taught in our schools; to give each student the best opportunity to develop his inherent potential his teaching should be adjusted to his needs; in order to plan wisely for such an important target in the war against poverty, an objective, dispassionate approach should be made to the noblest study of man – man himself – his similarities and differences, hereditary and environmental.

My intent at this Nobel Symposium has been to recognize one problem, to describe steps in its solution and to underline another. The serious problem of the world population explosion has resulted from technological developments in death control. Six years after the Draper report our nation is at last acting to help solve the problem in under-developed countries by birth control aid. After a century and a half we are now taking Malthus seriously. Must another worry, also centuries old, now be taken seriously? Will the technological explosion which creates our great, abundant society remove the last vestiges of survival of the fittest and lead to a reversal of evolution? Now that our 'real wages' are quadruple what they were a century ago and rising more than 2% per year, is this fear at last becoming a reality?

[21] In an interview entitled 'IQ Quality of US Population Declining' in *US News and World Report*, November 22, 1965, I suggest that facts on environment versus heredity might be obtained from a long term statistical study of adopted children. (In response to this article I received about seventy letters, all but one favorable to airing the worries I expressed.)

Man must forge his own destiny

It is clear that man's destiny will be shaped by the acts of man. The three great problems created by the exponential explosion of man's power over nature are nuclear war, the population explosion, and genetic deterioration. Lack of sufficient understanding of cause and effect relationships in human affairs and unwillingness to explore these with an objective, fact-finding approach constitutes an enormous threat to the future of mankind.

Thinking men prefer a destiny shaped by acts planned in terms of goals for human progress toward a richer, intellectual and artistic life for men better endowed to enjoy it. In performing acts planned for such goals, a society must inevitably subject its individuals to man-made laws, which should be based on rational understanding of the laws of nature which govern man's environment and his attributes as a form of life on earth. Wise legislation can best be made by governments supported by voting populations who use rational reasoning, based on known facts, to reach their decisions as citizens.

The central purpose of our educational system should be to develop a citizen's rational powers and to equip him to understand causal relationships, especially as they apply to man. The greatest obstacle in man's future evolution at the present time is lack of public education on the fact that man is a mammal and subject to known biological laws. The uninformed attitude about the genetic aspect of man as an animal is reminiscent of the ignorance of a century ago about the nature of life. Educated people were slow to accept Pasteur's definitive experiments of disproof of the spontaneous generation of living organisms. In due course these experiments founded modern sanitation.

The coming generation in America will be far more objective about the genetic nature of man, because of the improvement in High School teaching about the biology of the human species.

A great step forward has been taken by the textbooks prepared by the Biological Sciences Curriculum Study, of which Dr Bentley Glass of this symposium has been the Chairman. The forthright presentation of the possibility of genetic deterioration and of the population explosion and the relationship to human evolution brought forth in this book will contribute toward future generations the ability of to use their reasoning powers more wisely for the future evolution of man.

This symposium on *Genetics and the Future of Man* at Gustavus Adolphus College is a rationally-planned, farsighted and courageous act. It is the act of thinking men who prefer a destiny shaped by acts planned in terms of goals of human progress. It should contribute to the important goal of introducing subject matter relative to man's genetic future into the school system of America and into the thinking of Americans and other thoughtful people throughout the world. I regard it as a rare privilege to have had the opportunity as a participant to try to strike a blow intended to help forge a finer destiny for man.

PAUL RAMSEY

Moral and religious implications of genetic control

DR PAUL RAMSAY *was born in Menderhall, Mississippi, in 1913. He was graduated from Millsaps College in 1935 and earned his BD and PhD degrees from Yale in 1940 and 1943 respectively. He taught history, social science and philosophy at Millsaps College, social philosophy at Yale and Christian Ethics at Garrett Theological Seminary, Northwestern University before joining the Princeton University faculty. His acknowledged stature as a leader of thought in religion and ethics and the social sciences is reflected by the distinguished chair he holds at Princeton, the Harrington Spear Paine Chair in Religion, to which position he was appointed in 1957. Among his publications are 'Basic Christian Ethics'; 'War and the Christian Conscience'; 'How Shall Modern War be Justly Conducted'; 'Christian Ethics and the Sit-In'; and 'Nine Modern Moralists' which includes chapters on Dostoievski, Marx, Sartre, Reinhold Niebuhr, H. Richard Niebuhr, Paul Tillich, Emil Brunner, Jacques Maritain and Edmond Cahn. He served as President of the American Society of Christian Social Ethics in the United States and Canada in 1962 and 1963.*

The eugenic movement of the late nineteenth and early twentieth century was based in the main upon biological and socioscientific misinformation or lack of information, and – what is worse – upon parochial if not indeed élitist and racial views of the ideal type of man. An excellent history of this movement is Mark H. Haller's *Eugenics: Hereditarian Attitudes in American Thought.*[1] To read this book is to conclude, with R.S. Morison, Director of Medical and Natural Sciences at The Rockefeller Foundation, that 'the thing that has saved man from his limited visions in the past has been the difficulty of devising suitable means for reaching them.'[2] The culmination or abuse of eugenics in the ghastly Nazi experiments would seem to be sufficient to silence forever proposals for genetic control.

However, this is not the case, and for two reasons. First, contemporary geneticists are increasingly being driven to varying

[1] New Brunswick, N.J.: Rutgers University Press, 1963.

[2] Comments on Genetic Evolution, in Hudson Hoagland and Ralph W. Burhoe, eds., *Evolution and Man's Progress*. New York: Columbia University Press, 1962, p. 41. 'The troubled history of Utopian education warns us to take care in rebuilding human personality on infirm philosophy'; (Joshua Lederberg, 'Biological Future of Man', in *Man and His Future*, a Ciba Foundation Volume. J. and A. Churchill, Ltd., 104 Gloucester Place, London, 1963, p. 270). 'It must be pointed out rather emphatically that the genetic consequences of a eugenic program based on faulty or inadequate genetic knowledge could, in themselves, be as dangerous to our genetic endowment as radiation. It seems crystal clear that the implementation of some of the more bizarre eugenic recommendations of several decades ago would have been the worst sort of folly' (Bruce Wallace and Theodosius Dobhansky, *Radiation, Genes, and Man*. New York: Henry Holt and Co., 1959, p. 191).

degrees of gloom regarding the future of mankind because of the inexorable degeneration of the human genetic pool under the conditions of modern life. Secondly, since the second World War molecular biology has steadily increased the range and precision of our knowledge of genetics, which may make it possible to determine some, at least, of the objectives of a program of genetic improvement or of at least a program for preventing further genetic deterioration and which may also make it possible to devise suitable means for reaching these ends. Because of the ineluctable increase of the problem and of the knowledge that might afford some solution to it, it can safely be predicted that the future will see more rather than less discussion of proposals for genetic control.

Scientists will continue to debate these issues among themselves, and in the public forum. One scientist recently expressed a fitting sense of humility before the as yet unfathomed mystery of nature and nature's God, by asking his fellow scientists: 'If any one of us had devised a mechanism as complex as the situation of the human race, how would we feel about letting any of our colleagues monkey about with it, on the assumption that they knew as little about it as we know about the psychosocial mechanism?'[3] Still this would be a weak foundation, and probably a vanishing foundation, on which to base opposition to genetic control. It is for the scientist to pay attention to objections of this sort, and to call them to the attention of the public. The present state of scientific knowledge, however, and the enormous practical obstacles in the way, ought not to be given important place in a discussion of the moral and religious issues raised by present and future eugenic proposals.

It is incumbent upon me, however, to describe in summary fashion mankind's problematic genetic situation as this is understood by certain contemporary geneticists. This would

[3] Donald M. MacKay, in the Discussion of Eugenics and Genetics in *Man and His Future*.

not be so bad if from generation to generation a more or less stable pool of genes were in passage, with its particular balance of physical, mental and emotional strengths or defects. The fact is, however, that in addition to the load of genetic deficiency from the previous generation, one out of every five persons now living (20%) bears a deleterious mutation that has arisen with him and which he will pass on to or through any offspring he may have. The quality of human beings to be born could be maintained at its present level if and only if 20% become genetically extinct, either by failing to reach reproductive age or by not having children. The fact is that, because of our technical and medical competence and our proper concern for persons now alive, we are enabling people to reach the age of reproduction, and to reproduce when they do, in greater numbers than would have done so in former ages.

Normal balancing elimination is not hereby frustrated; it is only postponed. One can be sure that some future generation will begin to experience 20% genetic deaths. But then it will be too late, since by then those who manage to stay alive will be generally and seriously impaired because of the genetic load they bear. Unless some conscious selection is made and some positive or negative direction given to generation, natural selection will, as it were, return to do this by more inhumane means than men could devise. Just as it will be too late if we do not adopt deliberate control of the *numbers* to be born and if we simply wait for overcrowding of the planet and starvation to correct overpopulation, so with respect to the *quality* or the mental and physical strength of the population generally, it will be too late (and indeed it will be inhumane) if we do not adopt measures to counteract the genetic deterioration which modern civilization and humanitarianism foster and if we simply wait for balancing selection to overtake us and pull out the plug our hospitals now place in the way of the extinction of genetic defects.

Diabetes affords us a case in point. Diabetics formerly died early. After a cure was found in insulin, they were enabled to survive and lead useful lives. Since, however, they were not generally able to have children, these individuals were as genetically dead as if they had been stillborn. Now the safe delivery of the children of diabetic mothers is a commonplace in all our hospitals; and as a consequence the incidence of diabetes in the population is irreversibly increasing. 'Of course we can get along with a lot more diabetics, and with good medical care they can live happily and bear diabetic children of their own. But there is a limit beyond which this process cannot be carried, and if we consider not diabetes alone, but all other ills to which the human race is genetically heir, that limit is not far away.'[4]

The laws of genetics are general ones. They apply to all human endowments and dis-endowments. 'This prospect is not pleasant to contemplate, but insulin injections may, conceivably, have to be as common in some remote future as taking aspirin tablets is at present.'[5] We may be able to say of any one of the hereditary defects that can be singled out that, since (for example) eye glasses can remedy myopia, the effort that would be needed to eradicate or reduce the frequency of myopia would exceed that requisite to rectify the defect environmentally.'[6] We may even want to yield to the movement that has made wearing eye glasses romantically attractive, or at least not unattractive, thus feeding back rather than eliminating the genes for this weakness. But it is impossible to say this concerning the apparently irreversible increase of all the ills to which man is heir. This is the harsh reality the science of genetics discloses to us beneath the illusion

[4] Frederick Osborn, 'The Protection and Improvement of Man's Genetic Inheritance', in Stuart Mudd, ed., *The Population Crisis and the Use of World Resources*. Dr W. Junk Publishers, The Hague, 1964, p. 308.

[5] Th. Dobzhansky, *Mankind Evolving*. New Haven: Yale University Press, 1962, p. 332.

[6] *Ibid.*

(fostered by other sciences) that we are gradually conquering disease. What is good for the individual, and the generation now alive, is bad for the human race.

The geneticists I have read do not disagree as to the trend, but only concerning the degree or rapidity of the trend. In other words, they are pessimistic or optimistic within an ultimate genetic pessimism. Some say '...The facts of human reproduction are all gloomy...'[7] Others correct this by pointing out that medical science has mainly eliminated death before reproductive age from *infectious* diseases. These hold the opinion that a large fraction of *prenatal* and pre-adult deaths occur from recognizably genetic causes, and that genetic elimination is taking place at a good rate despite the rise in the longevity index.[8] There is also disagreement over whether mutations are always deleterious, and over whether the genetic cause of serious defects may not also be the cause of 'hybrid vigor' in the gene pool generally. But there is no disagreement about the trend, nor about the fact there is an exponential increase of microgenetic identification of genetic illnesses that could be either eliminated or greatly reduced in a generation or two.

Now, it may be objected that intellectual traits and emotional or moral capacities (in contrast to the color or the myopia of our eyes or our upright stature) are the product not of our genes but of our environment or our choices and will-power, and that in any case they may be markedly improved or corrected only by the training supplied by our human or cultural environment. To this is has to be replied that hereditary physical diseases and defects are curable no less than infectious diseases, and that the plasticity of intellectual capacities and emotional proclivities to environmental changes constitutes no special case. There is here

[7] Joshua Lederberg, 'The Biological Future of Man', in *Man and His Future*, p. 264.

[8] James F. Crow, 'Mechanisms and Trends in Human Evolution', in Hoagland and Burhoe, *op. cit.*, pp. 9 and 11.

at most a difference of degree. The premise or the finding of the science of genetics is that there is a genetic basis of mental and moral traits no less than of physical traits; and that the laws of gene frequency and the processes of mutation and selection apply no less to the 'higher' human attributes than they do to the 'lower'.[9] It is important to remember that genetic determination ('determiners' might be a better word) means genetic *endowment* or dis-endowment. It does not establish a regime of inexorable necessity to which man is subject. The relationship between genotype and the environment is a dynamic one. The genotype determines not rigid traits of the organism (the phenotype) but rather its norm of reaction to the environment. There is only disagreement concerning whether we yet know enough, or can know enough, about the genetic basis of complex moral and mental characteristics to do anything about the transmission of defects in these regards, excepts in extreme cases.

Moreover, the conditions of modern life are producing a 'negative feedback' in place of the positive feedback in strengths of mind and character which was the case during most of man's evolution, comparable to the negative feedback of physical defects modern medicine has produced.

Darwinian 'fitness' means reproductive fitness.[10] Of course, evolution has bred into mankind a capacity to give blow for blow, because the individuals most apt at this thereby preserved their genes. But so do individuals who are willing to give help for help. We must, therefore, correct the 'gladiatorial' image we have of the survival of the fittest. 'The fittest, in the evolutionary sense, is nothing more spectacular than the quiet, often unobtrusive fellow who, rather than spend his time in combat, produces, feeds, and teaches a large family of children.'[11]

[9] See, for example, H.J. Muller, 'Our Load of Mutations' in *The American Journal of Human Genetics*, II, 2 (June 1950), p. 165.

[10] Th. Dobzhansky, *op. cit.*, pp. 301, 330.

[11] Hampton L. Carson, *Heredity and Human Life*. New York: Columbia

Today, however, 'everyone is helped to live according to his need and to reproduce according to his greed, or lack of foresight, skill, or scruple.'[12] Cultural evolution no less than medical science has brought us around a turning point before which for long ages man was becoming physically, mentally and morally fitter but after which man may be becoming not only physically but mentally and morally less fit as well. 'I think there is no question whatsoever', said Professor Ernst Mayr of Harvard, 'that when there were smaller human groups, the selective premium on altruistic traits and cooperative traits that helped the survival of a well-integrated group must have been exceedingly high. Today, however, in a big metropolitan civilization, even highly antisocial behavior is not especially severely punished by natural selection.'[13] As is his wont, H.J. Muller draws the more negative conclusion: 'In fact, it seems not unlikely that in regard to the human faculties of the highest group importance – such as those needed for integrated understanding, foresight, scrupulousness, humility, regard for others, and self-sacrifice – cultural conditions today may be conducive to an actual lower rate of reproduction on the part of their possessors than of those with the opposite attributes.'[14]

Because of the negative feedback of genes for the poorer mental, emotional and moral traits and the suspension of the

University Press, 1963, p. 137. 'Any genetically determined trait, no matter what, which makes a man a better producer of a large and healthy family favors this particular line of descent just because this line makes a relatively large contribution to the composition of the gene pool of the next generation. Actually, the process can go on, and usually does, without any active struggle between the parties concerned.' *(Ibid.)*

[12] H.J. Muller, 'Should We Weaken or Strengthen our Genetic Heritage?' in Hoagland and Burhoe, *op. cit.*, p. 23.

[13] In the discussion printed in Hoagland and Burhoe, *op. cit.*, p. 57.

[14] H.J. Muller, 'The Guidance of Human Evolution', in *Perspectives in Biology and Medicine*, III, 1 (Autumn 1959). University of Chicago, 1959, p. 13.

selection for the better ones that went on for aeons, the crisis of our present-day civilization is a genetic crisis as well, and one that goes to the very *humanum* of man. This is an unfavorable, indeed a perilous, aspect of the fact that ours is now 'one world', which ordinarily you hear unqualifiedly praised as a consummation devoutly to be wished. As our common culture gradually becomes that of 'one world', *i.e.* as it extends to include the entire human gene pool, and if there is operative a negative feedback of genes for physical, mental and moral traits alike, then the failure of this culture is to be expected (like all civilizations of the past) – only this time the failure of the culture will mean failure for the entire human race (where before there were not only more or less encapculated 'primitive' tribes but great gene pools to begin the next advance).

Thus, by doing away with natural selection that used to keep us reasonably fit, by holding at bay the lethality of lethal genes and by weakening the disfavor formerly placed upon bearers of unsociable traits, mankind is allowing an insidious genetic deterioration that will leave us unfitter than we began.

This brings us, finally, to the effect of radiation on mutation rates. The discussion in recent years of hideous birth defects and monstrosities that would result for generations to come from nuclear war, or from high exposure to atmospheric fallout from testing, can be put in proper perspective only when we remember that none of these genetic defects are new occurrences. They are only the result of accelerating the *rate* of mutation that is going on all the time in human sex cells and accumulating in the pool of genes. The genetic effect of radioactive fallout is small by comparison with the genetic dilemma of 'normal' negative feedback.

It is also small by comparison with the consequences of the use of radiation energy for non-military purposes that will be normal for centuries to come. Exposure to radioactive fallout is decidedly smaller than from the medical and diagnostic use of radiation and the industrial use of atomic energy. The amount of radiation that will reach the reproductive cells from atmospheric testing is only about a hundredth as much per individual in the Unites States as that from medical diagnosis.[15] Assuming that ten generations pass before the end of this age of nuclear energy, *i.e.* before mankind learns to make direct use of solar energy as before he took his power from the sun in the form of fossil fuels, the exposure would lead to 30 million genetic deaths if one foolishly calculated the number literally for time without end; and on a more significant calculation, for, say, twenty generations or 600 years before the solar age, it would lead to 180000 genetic deaths per generation or 6000 annually – at the end of which span of time 90% of the induced mutants would still remain to be eliminated.[16] Plus, of course, a generally weakened population. Thus, on all counts the present age seems to be genetically debasing.

Now, 'we are all fellow mutants together';[17] and the question before us is: What are we going to do about our genetic dilemma? There is one and only one way of avoiding the 'fiasco of a full fledged resumption of ordinary natural selection. That method, whether we like it or not, is purposive control over reproduction'[18] – over its quality no less than over its quantity.

If there is a solution to the genetic problem, it will consist of finding some acceptable means of reducing the genetic load, or at least halting the increase of this load. To reduce the genetic load or to prevent further genetic deterioration, one would have to lower the mutation rate (or perform some operation that would cause back-mutation) and-or increase the elimination rate.

[15] H.J. Muller, *Man's Future Birthright*. University of New Hampshire, Feb., 1958, p. 14.
[16] *Ibid.*, pp. 128, 133, 143, 144.
[17] H.J. Muller, 'Our Load of Mutations' in *The American Journal of Human Genetics*, II, 2 (June 1950), p. 169.
[18] *Ibid.*, p. 150.

This brings us to the two sorts of proposals for genetic control that are possible today or are envisioned as future possibilities.

(1) The first is some direct attack upon the deleterious mutated gene, either by what is called 'genetic surgery', 'micro-surgery' or 'nano-surgery'[19] or by the introduction of some anti-mutagent chemical that will cause the gene to mutate back or will eliminate it from among the causes of genetic effects. At some time in the near or distant future this may be the means employed in a program of 'negative' or 'preventive' eugenics. This method could also be employed to induce or *direct* mutation in a program of 'progressive' eugenics or 'positive' genetic improvement.

(2) The second sort of available means arises from focusing attention upon the 'phenotype' and not the 'genotype': eugenically directed birth control, 'parental selection', 'germinal choice', or gross 'empirical' selection for traits in human reproduction. The means available for accomplishing this could be used either in a program of 'breeding in' desired traits ('progressive' or 'positive' eugenics) or in a program of 'breeding out' undesired traits ('preventive' or 'negative' eugenics). Such means would be the control of conception by persons advised to do so by hereditary clinics, voluntary sterilization, artificial insemination for eugenic reasons with semen from a non-husband donor, sometimes called 'pre-adoption' (AID), 'foster pregnancy', which is the reverse of AID and may indeed be arranged so as to produce an individual whose genetic inheritance is neither that of the husband nor that of the wife who is 'host' – I should say, 'hostess' – during the parturation of the fetus, or, finally, parthenogenesis (scientifically induced virgin birth).

Thus, the ethical question or questions to be raised concern

[19] These terms are used by H. J. Muller, 'Means and Aims in Human Genetic Betterment', in Tracy M. Sonneborn, ed., *The Control of Human Heredity and Evaluation*. New York: The Macmillan Co., 1965. 'Nano' designates a scale a thousand times smaller than 'micro'.

the morality of the ends or objectives to be adopted in any program of genetic control, the morality of 'progressive' eugenics in comparison with the morality of 'preventive' eugenics, the morality of parental selection in comparison with the morality of genetic surgery, and the morality of each of the specific means that are currently proposed and are apt to come into greater prominence in future discussion. Such are the considerations that have to be brought under scrutiny if anyone asks about the moral and religious implications of this science-based issue.

First, however, it will be illuminating to ask: what is the ethics actually governing in proposals for genetic control, and among geneticists themselves?

In its account of the origin of the unique, unrepeatable individual person, the science of genetics seems to have resolved an ancient theological dispute. The human individual first comes into existence as a minute informational speck which resulted from the random combination of a great number of still more minute informational specks derived from the genetic pool which his parents passed on to him at the moment of impregnation. His subsequent pre-natal and post-natal development may be described as a process of becoming what he already is from the moment he was conceived. There are a virtually unimaginable number of combinations of paternal and maternal genes that did not come to be when these were refused and he began to be. It is, therefore, virtually certain that no two individuals (with a single exception, to be mentioned in a moment) in the whole course of mankind's existence have ever had or will ever have the same genotype.[20] This is a form of 'traducianism', *i.e.* the

[20] Wallace and Dobzhansky, *Radiation, Genes, and Man*, p. 32.

theory that the never-to-be-repeated individual human being (the 'soul' is the religious word for him) was drawn forth from his parents at the time of conception.

Thus, science seems to have demonstrated what theology never could. Of course, pre-scientific notions are still believed by a great many people. Our law, for example (which seems always to be based on antique notions and to be in need of reform), takes the moment of birth to be the moment after which there is a 'man alive' (for which the evidence is air in the lungs). After that he is what he is becoming; and only then is 'murder' possible as a crime. Where 'abortion' is defined as a criminal offense in our legal system, this is a separate category of proscribed actions. Abortion is not legally prohibited as a species of murder, but because of the law's presumption that society has a stake in the prehuman material out of which the unique individual is born. Or again, 'superstitious' people – Roman Catholics, for example – still may debate and do debate whether the unique, never-to-be-repeated human being begins with impregnation ('traducianism') or at the moment fetal life becomes independently animate or self-moving in the womb ('creationism'). If animation is the moment when the individual offspring first begins to be what he is to become, and launches on a course of becoming what he already is, then direct abortion after animation would be – morally, not legally – a species of murder; while direct abortion before animation, if this is defined as an offense, would fall within a class of far less serious invasions of the 'nature' of our generative faculties ('adultery').

Modern genetics, however, seems to have settled all this when it demonstrated if not quite the unrepeatability at least the never-to-be-repeated character of that first informational speck each of us once was and still is in every cell and attribute.

I may pause here to raise the question whether a scientist has not an entirely 'frivolous conscience' who, faced with the awesome technical possibility that soon human life may be able to be created in the laboratory and then either be terminated or preserved in existence as an experiment, or who gets up at scientific gatherings and gathers to himself newspaper headlines by urging upon his colleagues that they must prepare for that scientific accomplishment by giving attention to the 'ethical' questions this raises – if he is not at the same time, and in advance, prepared to stop the whole procedure should the 'ethical finding' concerning this fact-situation turn out to be, for any serious conscience, murder. It would perhaps be better for the ethical issues to have been not raised, than not to raise them in earnest.

This genetic account of the origin of human individuality discloses its need for supplementation (though, of course, not its incorrectness as one of the sciences of man) in the case of the single exception to this contemporary traducianism. This is the case of identical twins. Identical twins have the same genotype. They arise from the same informational speck. Yet each is and knows he is a unique, unrepeatable human person. Something he is that he never was by virtue of his genotype. Something he became, at some time and in some manner, for which the genes drawn from his parents do not account or that he was not already from the fission following that original conception.

To explain the difference between identical twins one may resort to differences in the environment, which are great even in the normal case of identical twins who grow up in the same household. This is a modern formulation of the theory of 'creationism': the Environment, the Maker of all twin-differences, and the Creator of a twin-person's unsharable individual being, 'infused' this into the original hereditary material which was the same genotype. Thus, the human person becomes himself from what he never was at the beginning or by genetic determination alone; and it does not matter that he is in process of becoming who he is for the duration of an entire lifetime in one environment or another. Also, it would not matter that you cannot tell exactly when, in the pre-natal environment, if you kill one identical twin fetus you kill not him but his brother because each is, as it were, his own twin and because each has, so far, no more of his individual humanity than the identical genotype.

The question to be raised is whether two such sciences are more sufficient than one (though both are doubtless correct). Does the drawing forth of the person from his informational speck and from his environment give a complete account of man, his uniqueness, individuality and unrepeatability? According to the total genetic-environmental vision of life, it would seem that, given infinite time, all possibilities would be actualized – including events that are so extremely unlikely as to be almost inconceivable, such as that two individuals of the same genotype might arise from two different combinations of sexual determiners and who would be, as it were, 'identical twins' even though they are born a hundred thousand years apart in time, or including the supposable case of those genotypes we actually know to be identical twins happening to be brought up in separate but *identical* environments. The latter would differ only in their *that-ness* and *where-ness* as similar sticks and stones or atoms and neutrons may differ, but they would not be significantly distinct in their *what-ness* or *who-ness*. Thus, from some of its tendencies, modern thinking would accomplish a return to the vision of those ancients who believed 'that the same periods and events of time are repeated [or are, at least, essentially repeatable]; as if, for example, the philosopher Plato, having taught in the school at Athens which is called the Academy, so, numberless ages before, at long but certain intervals, this same Plato and the same school, and the same disciples existed, and so also are to be repeated during the countless cycles that are yet to be...'[21]

[21] Augustine, *The City of God*, Bk. XII, ch. XIII. *The New York Times*, December 26, 1964, reported an incident that happened on Christmas day

Now, I am sensible that there is a great distance from the conclusion of genetics and environmentalism that an identical human individual is '*almost* certain' not to be repeated to the conclusion of the ancients that the repeatable *will* certainly be repeated.[22] But from the idea that the individuals who appear in biological evolution have such a genetic constitution that it is *exceedingly unlikely* that any one of them will ever recur, there is an equally large leap needed ever to arrive at the notion that in himself the individual has uniqueness of such a kind that he *cannot* be repeated or replayed.

I do not propose to develop here a counter-thesis concerning the nature of man, or to try to demonstrate that Theology is still the Queen of the sciences. It is more important to point out that if and only if there is a more adequate view of man will ethics be possible and that where there is ethics there will be implied in it a more adequate view of man than the one we have just reviewed.

in Louisville, Kentucky, which may be compared with the realization of genetic improbabilities. In a game of bridge it happened that *all four players* were dealt hands each containing the 13 cards of the same suit. According to the World Almanac, the chance that *one player* in a bridge game will get 13 cards of the same suit is one in 158753389900. The odds against all four players getting the same suit is not given. These odds must be tremendous, yet this is what happened. When one remembers that such highly unlikely events can happen early in a series of deals rather than after an indefinite number of deals, then it would seem entirely possible that individuals other than 'identical twins' have already been 'dealt' the same genotype in the course of human history; and that these genotypes may be called upon to reappear again.

[22] The ancients were, quite correctly, possessed by a 'spirit of melancholy' (Nietzsche) over the eternal recurrence, because this view entailed the inexorable disappearance of the best as well as its return in the cycles. Having derived from the Christian doctrine of providence the idea that human history has *linear* significance if it has any at all, a modern geneticist is likely, instead, to be afflicted with unmitigated gloom as he faces the prospect of irreversable linear genetic degeneration.

The geneticists I have read are themselves instances of this. There is no ethics to be found among the contents of any science. There is, nevertheless, a morality of science. Geneticists, notably, do not treat the individual as if he were merely the carrier of the genetic determiners that will be productive of the next and future generations. They do not reduce him to the red color or the sweetness of a ripe apple fallen to the ground (of which it can perhaps be said that it is 'almost certain' there has never been another quite like it) which when engorged by an animal who defecates the seed at a distance from the parent tree secures the spread of the species. Geneticists do not treat the individual as if he were that plus what the environment makes him. Few are the geneticists who in their proposals concerning genetic control toy with the idea that there might be a chemical added to the water supply that would make everyone sterile, and then a second chemical that would reverse the effect of the first be given by the government to selected persons 'licensed to bear children'.[23] Notably, the contemporary geneticist, Professor H.J. Muller, who is most pessimistic about our 'genetic load' and its rapid deterioration under the conditions of modern life and who is therefore most radical in his proposals for genetic improvement is also the most insistent upon the use of voluntary means only and upon achieving his imperative goals by reliance on the exercise of responsible human freedom.[24]

[23] See Crick in the discussion recorded in *Man and His Future*, pp. 275–276.

[24] It is true that H.J. Muller sometimes writes as if he utterly disparages the *present* individual human being. 'We thus arrive', he writes, 'at a picture of humankind as a creature living between an enormous past and perhaps a still longer future, fabricated out of inner microsomic immensities that he cannot directly perceive, but on the surface of which, as it were, his awareness floats as on a film, while facing outer vistas of a staggering grandeur. He thus stands poised among a series of abysses...' Still the whole dignity of this 'awareness' that 'floats as on a film' evidently consists in the fact that he knows this, and can act accordingly, for Muller concludes the foregoing

We shall have to ask what is the *source* and what is the rational or other *ground* of the ethics that governs eugenic proposals. The source of this morality is doubtless the atmospheric humanism and the liberal progressivism which sustains any ostensibly science-based ethics today. Anyone who reads the numerous, morally-impassioned writings of H.J. Muller on the subject of eugenics, composed as these are by a man who can almost hear the 'sound' of deleterious mutations going on all around him and who knows these increasingly fail to be eliminated from the

sentence with the words: '...yet by searching and studying these abysses, he is finding means of traversing them' (*The World View of Moderns*, University of Illinois 50th Anniversary Lecture Series. University of Illinois Press, 1958, p. 15). Again, Muller writes that 'a more realistic consideration... will usually show... that we have about as much to be ashamed of in ourselves genetically as to be proud of. It will reveal us as being one small even though potentially significant mote in the whole human assemblage, a mote constitutionally inclined to over-estimate itself' ('Better Genes for Tomorrow', in Stewart Mudd, *op. cit.*, p. 323).

It is true that, as this passage shows, obsessed by the gloomy facts about mankind's genetic load, Muller does not accept (as Augustine said of the Manichees) 'with good and simple faith this good and simple reason why the good God created' such a world as this – because, for all the mutations corrupting it, its basic nature still is good. It is also true that, like Engels, he believes in his pessimism that everything that is real within the realm of generation is bound to become unreasonable after a while; hence it is already by definition unreasonable; and in his optimism he believes that everything that is reasonable within the hearts of men may become real, however much it may contradict the existing seeming genetic reality. Still, nothing in this excludes the governing influence of the ethics described above. The man of the future will be both a product and a conscious agent whose dignity is exhibited by his transcendent control over his own evolution. And while now man is only a mote among the contents of genetics, he is also a thinking mote who can rise above all this and intend the world as a geneticist or whose noblest action would be to sacrifice his existing seeming reality to that future ideal.

human genetic pool, is apt to exclaim that there has been nothing like it since the French philosopher Condorcet wrote his treatise on human progress in a prison cell in Paris within the sound of the guillotine clicking away its fell work amid the roars of a degenerate mob!

When one asks concerning the rational or other grounds of the ethics of voluntarism and responsible freedom, the humanitarism and progress doctrine, that evidently is governing in proposals for genetic improvement, and when one asks for an account of the respect for the uniqueness and dignity of the human individual manifest by and entailed in this ethic, no sufficient answer can be found in the science of genetics itself or in the truth it discovers concerning the biological world. The answer must be found (and for science this is the final answer) among the presuppositions of there being any science of genetics at all, not among its contents. There is an ethic and there is a view of man that makes science possible. Man must be, his mind must be, and his virtues or values must be of a certain order for there to be the preconditions of any scientific knowledge at all. And as Kant long ago knew, anything that is a *necessary* presupposition of scientific knowledge must be as certainly valid as that scientific knowledge itself is true.

It is quite obvious that the voluntariness upon which Muller's program is based has more substantial foundations in his estimate of man than the basis he once asserted this to have in the 'genetic feedback' of servile traits a compulsory program would produce. '...A dictatorship', he wrote, 'though it might hoodwink, cajole and compel its subjects into participation in its [eugenic] programme, would try to create a servile population uncomplainingly conforming to their ruler's whims. *That would constitute an evolutionary emergency* much more immediate and ominous than any gradual degeneration occasioned by a negative cultural feedback.' ('Genetic Progress by Voluntarily Conducted Germinal Choice', in *Man and His Future*, p. 257, italics added). One has to be a scientific *humanist* even to know what constitutes an 'evolutionary emergency'.

'All biological species have evolved, but only man knows that he has evolved.'[25] Biologically speaking, man is a creature with a certain favorable or unfavorable genetic inheritance; but, still biologically speaking, man is the geneticist who knows this. Genetically speaking, we may say *à la Pascal*, 'Man is a thinking mutant. It is not necessary for the whole universe to arm itself to crush him. A vapour, a drop of water, a mutant gene, is sufficient to slay him. But were his genetic load to crush him, man would still be nobler than that which kills him, for he knows that he dies, he knows all the truths of microgenetics and he foreknows that he may die of the degenerative forces accumulating in the genetic substructure from which came also his genetic superiority over other forms of life, while the universe and the lethal genes know nothing of the advantage they have over him. Thus our whole dignity consists in thought.'[26] Thus, the ethics of science applicable to this science-based issue is the fruit of consciously intending the world as a geneticist; and the view of man here entailed is that of man the truth-seeking, truth-finding and truth-using animal. Man is the free and intentional *subject* of all this. He is not merely the object discovered among the contents of the science of genetics. Rather is he essentially the one who knows all that, and who may use his knowledge for the good of other such persons. There is a genuinely humanistic ethics at work in proposals for genetic

[25] Wallace and Dobzhansky, *op. cit.*, p. 194.

[26] Cf. Pascal's 'thinking reed' passage: *Pensées*, 347. H.J. Muller: 'By working in functional alliance with our genes, we may attain to modes of thought and living that today would seem inconceivably god-like. In this expression the word "thought" had advisedly been set before "living". For thought is the distinctive and central mode of existence of man, the new mode of expression of the genes, and in the beings who succeed us if we win out, thought will ever more truly come into its own' ('Man's Place in the Living Universe', an address at Indiana University, June 9, 1956, Indiana University Publications, 1956, p. 24).

control which, as a consequence, find it contradictory (not to what the sciences in their contents say constitutes man, but) to the presuppositions of the very possibility of such scientific knowledge if it is proposed to treat the human individual as a mere object of genetic or environmental determination to be imposed coersively upon him.

J. Bronowski formulated in general terms the *presuppositional* status of a scientific ethic (which must be at least as valid as any of the material findings of science) in his book *Science and Human Values*, where he undertook to show 'the place of science in the canons of conduct which it has still to perfect.'[27] In fact he showed the place of certain canons of conduct in science. He demonstrated that these canons of conduct are the *necessary* presupposition of their being any place whereon for science itself to stand. In fact, as Bronowski wrote, he brought under study 'the [moral] conditions for the success of science and [found] in them the values of man which science would have had to invent afresh if man had not otherwise known them.'[28] Chief among these canons of conduct is 'the habit of truth' which has made our society as surely as it has made the linotype machine or Darwin's *Origin of Species*.[29] Another is the knowing-community that science presupposes, and the fact that verification has no meaning if it is assumed to be carried out by one man without any reference to this community of discourse.[30] Thus, truth depends on 'truthfulness' and upon 'a principle which binds society together, because without it the individual would be helpless to tell the true from the false.' Bronowski formulates a categorical imperative which is a necessary presupposition or the condition of the possibility of scientific knowledge: 'We

[27] First published in 1956. New York: Harper and Bros., Torchbook edition, 1959, p. 13.
[28] *Ibid.*
[29] *Op. cit.*, p. 61.
[30] *Op. cit.*, pp. 72–73.

OUGHT to act in such a way that what IS true can be verified as such.'[31]

The virtues and standards this requires, however much scientists may sometimes fail to achieve them, are nevertheless not an alien professional code sought to be imposed. Instead, the virtues prerequisite to science 'spring from the pith and sap of the work they regulate'; the real essence of it is brought against any existential distortions. Thus, the values of science derive neither from the personal superiority of its participants nor from 'finger-wagging codes'; 'they have grown out of the practice of science, because they are the inescapable conditions for its practice.'[32] 'An ethics for science... derives directly from its own activity.'[33] This ethics includes the values of tolerance and democracy, since 'science cannot survive without justice and honor and respect between man and man.'[34] Finally, by this presuppositional method of justification, Bronowski affirms the unique value of the individual: science 'must prize the search above the discovery and the thinking (and with it the thinker) above the thought. In the society of scientists each man, by the process of exploring for the truth, has earned a dignity more profound than his doctrine. A true society is sustained by the sense of human dignity.'[35] Thus again it is manifestly the case

[31] *Op. cit.*, p. 74. In the 'body' or 'fellowship' of scientists 'the power of virtue' must be operative: '...All scholars in their work are... oddly virtuous. They do not make wild claims, they do not cheat, they do not try to persuade at any cost, they appeal neither to prejudice nor to authority, they are often frank about their ignorance, their disputes are fairly decorous, they do not confuse what is being argued with race, politics, sex or age, they listen patiently to the young and to the old who both know everything' (p. 75).

[32] *Op. cit.*, p. 77.

[33] *Op. cit.*, p. 80.

[34] *Op. cit.*, p. 81.

[35] *Op. cit.*, p. 83.

that, as Pascal said, 'our whole dignity consists in thought' – no matter what the 'discovery' or the 'doctrine' (*e.g.* the science of genetics, objectively viewed) says about man.

This, then, is the ethics that governs most genetic proposals. It is an ethics that is rationally grounded in the fact that, genetically speaking, man is at least the geneticist – and all else that this implies.

Upon observing this to be the case, we may well find it significant that when Bronowski writes that science would have had to invent these values if they did not already exist he said: 'if man had not otherwise *known* them.'[36] Such an ethics is the fruit of intending the world as a man in the community of men, and not simply the fruit of intending the world as a scientist in the community of scientists. Doubtless in the present age it is important that science confirms these human values, that it perfects them, and 'in societies where these values do not exist, science has had to create them.'[7] Still, this ethic must already be grounded in a more adequate understanding of what it means to be a man than is contained in or can be forthcoming from the 'doctrine' of the individual's genetic origins (however correct this may be), or for that matter from, in itself, 'the habit of truth.'[38] Western science is itself the product of a certain civili-

[36] *Op. cit.*, p. 13 (italics added).

[37] *Op. cit.*, p. 81.

[38] It is manifestly absurd for Bronowski to explain William Wilberforce's successful opposition to the slave trade by saying: 'He had at bottom only one ground: that dark men are men. *A century and more of scientific habit by then had made his fellows find that true*...' (p. 60, italics added). After all, Wilberforce was a Bishop! Similarly, can anyone believe the following passages to be at all adequate accounts of two great moments in the history of British and American liberties? (1) 'Not the high talk about the divine right of kings, and not the Bill of Rights, but their test in experience. England would have been willing to live by either concept, as it has been willing to live by Newton or by Einstein: it chose the one which made

zation and its values, which are 'otherwise known' if they are ever known to be valid; science may only 'perfect' them and in other cultures help to 'create' them.

Finally, it is pertinent to make this concluding observation, without prejudice and without forgetting the extraordinary richness of those values which can be shown to be the necessary presupposition of there being any science at all, and without disparaging the depth in the corollary that the individual's whole dignity consists in thought. A great deal is here asserted to be morally known that is not simply contained in the contents of any science. Still, this is a limiting view; and the limits arise from the fact that the ethics is a fruit of intending the world as a scientist and not expressly from intending the world as a man among men, much less from intending the world as a Christian or as a Jew. This accounts for the fact that when they begin to describe those human qualities to be selected and bred into the race of men, geneticists write remarkably as if they are describing the attributes of mind and of character that would make a good geneticist, or at least a good community of scientists. Acknowledging that these are notably humanistic values, still there are other modes of being human.

society work of itself, without constraint' (p. 55). Surely, the extension through centuries of struggle of the meaning of Magna Carta's 'No freeman shall...' was a process by which men more clearly apprehended and put into exercise the meaning of liberty which was 'otherwise known.' (2) 'We see it [the test of experienced fact] cogently in the Declaration of Independence, which begins in the round Euclidean manner: "We hold these truths to be self-evident", but which takes the justification for its action at last from "a long train of abuses and usurpations": the colonial system had failed to make a workable society' (p. 56). Surely, any school child knows whence our Founding Fathers took the justification for their actions at last; and that, without knowledge of the inalienable rights of man bestowed by nature's God, they could not have known abuses to be abuses or usurpations to be usurpations.

In order to analyse the moral implications of genetic control for western religions it is necessary to lift up to view certain aspects of what it means to intend the world as a Christian or as a Jew. These also are modes of being human and how values are 'otherwise known' in this world and ethical judgments made. On the assumption that it is a Christian *subject* who has come into the possession of all this genetic knowledge and who faces our genetic dilemma, what will be the attitude he takes up toward eugenic proposals? Two ingredients are of chief importance. First, we have to contrast biblical or Christian eschatology with genetic eschatology, and observe how these practical proposals may change their hue when shifted from one ultimate philosophy of history to the other. This will be the matter of the present section of this paper. Then, secondly and in the following section, we have to explore the bearing which the Christian understanding of the union between the personally unitive purpose and the procreative purpose of human sexual relations (sex as at once an act of love and an act of procreation) may have upon the question of the means to be used in genetic control.

The writings of H.J. Muller give the most vivid portrayal of the genetic *cul-de-sac* into which the human race is heading. He describes, in fact, a genetic Apocalypse. His fellow geneticists can correct, if they must, the extremism of this vision. For the purpose of making clear, however, how one intends the world as a Christian even in the face of such an apocalyptic account of the End toward which we are proceeding, or which is coming upon us, it is better to leave the vision unaltered and assume it to be a true account of the scientific facts.

Within a period of a few million years, according to Muller, provided that during this period our medical men have been able to continue to work with the kind of perfection they desire, 'the then existing germ cells of what were once human beings would be a lot of hopeless, utterly diverse genetic monstrosities.' Long before that, 'the job of ministering to infirmities would come to consume all the energy that society could muster', leaving no surplus for general or higher cultural purposes.[39] People's time and energy would be mainly spent in an effort 'to live carefully, to spare and prop up their own feebleness, to soothe their inner disharmonies and, in general, to doctor themselves as effectively as possible'. Everyone will be an invalid, and everyone's accumulated internal disability would amount to lethality if he had to live under primitive conditions.[40] If any breakdown occurs in the complex hospital system civilization will have become, mankind will be thrown back into a wretchedness with which his primitive beginnings cannot be compared.

'Our descendants' natural biological organization would in fact have disintegrated and have been replaced by complete disorder. Their only connection with mankind would then be the historical one that we ourselves had after all been their ancestors and sponsors, and the fact that their once-human material was still used for the purpose of converting it, artificially, into some semblance of man. However, it would in the end be far easier and more sensible to manufacture a complete man *de novo*, out of appropriately chosen raw materials, than to try to refashion into human form those pitiful relics which remained. For all of them would differ inordinately from one another, and each would present a whole series of most intricate research problems, before the treatments suitable for its own unique set of vagaries could be decided upon.'[41]

[39] H.J. Muller, 'The Guidance of Human Evolution', in *Perspectives in Biology and Medicine*, p. 11.
[40] H.J. Muller, 'Our Load of Mutations', in *The American Journal of Genetics*, pp. 146, 171.
[41] *Ibid.*, p. 146. Cf. also H.J. Muller, 'Should We Strengthen or Weaken our Genetic Heritage?' in Hoagland and Burhoe, *op. cit.*, p. 27. It seems not

It is unreasonable to expect medicine to keep up with the problem (especially because medical men themselves in that near or distant future will be subject to the same genetic decomposition); and 'at long last even the most sophisticated techniques available could no longer suffice to save men from their biological corruptions'[42] (and, again, I add to Muller's assumptions, medicine in that future could not be all that sophisticated, because of the genetic deterioration of the medical men who would be alive in the generation before the genetic *eschaton*).

Stripped of rhetoric, this means that, according to the genetic Apocalypse, there shall come a time when *there will be none like us to come after us*. There have been other such scientific visions of the future. Whether this results from the pollution of the atmosphere and the streams by industrial refuse, or of the atmosphere by strontium-90, or from a collision of planets, the burning up of the earth or, alternatively, the entropy of energy until our planet enters the eternal night of a universe run down, these scientific predictions without exception portray a planet no longer fit for human habitation or a race of men no longer fit to live humanly. Because these are science-based Apocalypses, the gruesome details of the 'last days' can be filled in, and our imaginations heightened in its apprehension of the truth concerning physical nature and the prospects of human history in the one dimension that is scientifically known to us. All these visions quite realistically teach that there will come a time when there will be none like us to come after us. It is as obvious as the ages are long that it is an infirm philosophy which teaches that 'man can be courageous only so long as he knows he is

a sufficient answer to all this to reply: 'Norway rats... have been kept in laboratories since some time before 1840 and 1850... But it does not follow that laboratory rats are decadent and unfit; nor does it follow that the "welfare state" is making man decadent and unfit – to live in a welfare state!' (Th. Dobzhansky, *op. cit.*, p. 326).

[42] H. J. Muller, 'Better Genes for Tomorrow', in Stuart Mudd, *op. cit.*, p. 315.

survived by those who are like him, that [in *this* sense] he fulfils a role in something more permanent than himself.'[43] So far as concerns the capacity of scientific eschatology (with the single exception of the view that human history is *eternal*) to place in jeopardy courage and all other values that are grounded in the future of the human generations, it does not matter whether the End comes early or late. Nor do the gruesome details do more than heighten the imagination. They do not add to the ultimate meaninglessness to which all human affairs were reduced when meaning came to rest in the temporal future (unless that future is foreknown to be eternal – and, when you think it through, that too is a melancholy prospect). All that can be said to the credit of the genetic Apocalypse or to the credit of any science-based eschatology, is that it makes *impressive* the truth that was already contained in the thought that men live in 'one world'.

Anyone who intends the world or perceives the world as a Christian will have to reply that he knew this all along; and that he has already taken into his system the idea that one day there will be none like us to come after us. Even gruesome details about what will happen in the 'last days' are not missing from the Christian's Apocalypse, even though admittedly these are not extrapolations from scientific facts or laws. The *Revelation of St. John* is still in the Bible; and even the so-called 'little apocalypse' (Mark 13 and parallels) had this to say: 'In those days shall be affliction, such as was not from the beginning of the creation which God created unto this time, neither shall be... But in those days, after that tribulation, the sun shall be darkened, and the moon shall not give her light, and the stars of heaven shall fall, and the powers that are in heaven shall be shaken' (Mark 13:19, 24–25). Stripped of rhetoric, there will be none like us to come after us on this planet.

This means that Christian hope into and through the future

[43] Hannah Arendt, quoted in *Worldview* editorial, Sept. 1958, p. 1.

depends not at all on denying the number or seriousness of the accumulating lethal mutations which Muller finds to be the case (let his fellow geneticists argue with him however they will).

Where genetics teaches that we are made out of genes and unto genes return, *Genesis* teaches that we are made out of the dust of the ground and unto dust we and all our seed return. Never has biblical faith and hope depended on denying or refusing to face any facts, either of history or of physical or biological nature. No natural or historical 'theodicy' was ever required to establish the providence of God, since this was not confined to the one dimension within which modern thought finds its limits.

It is as easy (and as difficult) to believe in God after Auschwitz as it was after Sennacherib came down like a wolf on the fold to besiege and destroy the people of God. The Jews who chanted as they went to meet their cremation, '*Ani Ma'amin...*' 'I believe with unswerving faith in the coming of the Messiah', uttered words appropriate also to that earlier occasion, and to all temporal occasions. It is as easy (and as difficult) to believe in God after Mendel and Muller as it was after Darwin or the dust of *Genesis*. Religious people have never denied, indeed they affirm, that God means to kill us all in the end, and in the end He is going to succeed. Anyone who intends the world as a Jew or as a Christian – to the measure in which this is his mode of being in the world – goes forth to meet the collision of planets or the running down of suns, and he exists toward a future that may contain a genetic Apocalypse with his eye fixed on another *eschaton*: '*Ani Ma'amin...*' 'I believe with unswerving faith in the coming of Messias'. He may take these words literally, or they may imaginatively express his conviction that men live in 'two cities' and not in one only. In no case need he deny whatever account science may give him of this city, this history or this world, so long as science does not presume to turn itself into a theology by blitzing him into believing it is the one and only Apocalypse.[44]

This does not mean a policy of inaction or mere negative 'acceptance' of trends in history or in biology on the part of anyone who is a Christian knowing-*subject* of all that he knows about the world. Divine determination, properly understood, imposes no iron law of necessity, no more than does genetic determination. Only the ultimate *interpretation* of all the action that is going on is different, and significantly different. We shall have to ask what practical difference this makes as one man goes about responding in all the action that comes upon him to the action of the laws of genetics while another goes about responding in all the action coming upon mankind to the action of God; or as one gives answers to the ultimate untrustworthiness of the force behind genetic trends while another answers with his life and choices to a trustworthiness beyond all real or seeming untrustworthy things.[45]

The differences are two – one pervasive and the other more precise. In the first instance, one has to notice the tone of as-

[44] In an article entitled 'Sex and People: A Critical Review' (*Religion and Life*, XXX, Winter, 1960–61, pp. 53–70), I sought to apply the edification to be found in Christian eschatology in refutation of those genial viewpoints sometimes propounded by Christians on the basis of a doctrine of creation, which hold that religious people *must* believe that God intends an abundant *earthly* life for every baby born and that we would deny His providence if in any measure we doubt that world population control combined with economic growthmanship can finally succeed in fulfilling God's direction of human life to this end. This is secular progressivism with religious overtones. Taken seriously enough, it can lead as well as any other utopianism to the adoption of any means to that end, the control of the world's population. In essence, an independent morality of means, or righteousness in conduct, is collapsed into utilitarianism when the *eschaton* or man's supernatural end is replaced by any future *telos*.

[45] The language of this paragraph is that of H. Richard Niebuhr, *The Responsible Self*. New York: Harper and Row, 1963.

sertive or declaratory optimism based on an ultimate and unrelieved pessimism that pervades the thought of some proponents of eugenics. The writings of H.J. Muller cannot be accounted for simply by the science of genetics, or even by the fact that his ethics is that of a man who intends the world as a scientist and finds the whole dignity of man to consist in thought. As such and in themselves these things might be productive of more serenity, or serenity in action. But it is the whole creation, as this is known in genetics to be effectively present today and into the future, that Muller is fighting. No philosophy since Bertrand Russell's youthful essay[46] has been so self-consciously built upon the firm foundations of an unyielding despair. Mankind is doomed unless positive steps are taken to regulate our genetic endowment; and so horrendous is the genetic load that it often seems that Muller means to say that mankind is doomed no matter what steps are taken. Yet his optimism concerning the solutions he proposes is no less evident throughout; and all the more so, the more it is clear that his solutions (dependent as they are upon voluntary adoption) are unequal to the task. His language soars, the author aspires higher, he challenges his contemporaries to nobler acts of genetic self-formation and improvement, all the more because of the abyss below. The abyss sets up such powerful wind currents that mankind seems destined to be drawn into it no matter how high we fly. These are some of the consequences of the fact when all hope is gone Muller hopes on *in despair*. An Abraham of genetic science, if one should arise, would be one who when all hope is gone hopes on *in faith*, and who therefore need neither fear the problem nor trust the solution of it too much.

The more precisely identifiable difference is the greater room there will be for an 'ethics of means' in the outlook of anyone who is oriented upon the Christian *eschaton* and not upon the

[46] 'A Free Man's Worship'. There is less posturing in Muller's despair, more in the optimism that floats over this despair, than in Russell.

genetic *cul-de-sac* alone. Anyone who intends the world as a Christian or as a Jew knows along his pulses that he is not bound *to succeed* in preventing genetic deterioration, any more than he would be bound to hold up entropy or prevent planets from colliding with this earth or the sun from cooling. He is under no necessity of *insuring* that those who come after us will be like us, any more than he is bound to *insure* that there will be those like us to come after us. He knows no such *absolute* command of nature or of nature's God. This does not mean that he will do nothing. But it does mean that as he goes about the urgent business of doing his duty in regard to future generations he will *not* begin with the desired *end* and deduce his obligation exclusively from this. He will not define *right* merely in terms of conduciveness to the good end; nor will he decide what *ought to be done* simply by calculating what actions are most likely to succeed in achieving the *absolutely imperative end* of genetic control or improvement.

The Christian knows no such absolutely imperative end that would justify any means. Therefore, as he goes about the urgent business of bringing his duty to people now alive more into line with his genetic duty to future generations, he will always have in mind the premise that there may be a number of things that might succeed better but which would be intrinsically wrong means for him to adopt. Therefore, he has a larger place for an ethics of means that is not wholly dependent on the ends of action. He knows that there may be a great many actions that would be wrong to put forth in this world no matter what good consequences are expected to follow from them – especially if these consequences are thought of simply along the line of temporal history where, according to the Christian, success is not promised mankind by either Scripture or sound reason. He will approach the question of genetic control with a category of 'cruel and unusual means' that he is prohibited to employ, just as he knows there are 'cruel and unusual punishments' that are not to be employed in the penal code. He will ask, What are right means? no less than he asks, What are the proper objectives? And he will know in advance that any person or any society or age that expects ultimate success where ultimate success is not to be found is peculiarly apt to devise extreme and morally illegitimate means for getting there. This, he will know, can easily be the case if men go about making themselves the lords and creators of the future race of men. He will say, of course, of any historical and future-facing action in which he is morally obliged to engage: 'Only the end can justify the means' (as Dean Acheson recently said of foreign policy). Because, however, he is not wholly engaged in future-facing action or oriented upon the future consequences with the entirety of his being, he will immediately add (as Acheson did): 'This is not to say that the end justifies any means, or that some ends can justify anything.'[47] An ethics of means not derived from or dependent upon the objectives of action is the immediate fruit of knowing that men have another End than the receding future contains.

The ethics which, as we have seen, governs genetic proposals says as much. A fruit of intending the world as a geneticist is an ethics whose means are determined by the values of free-will and thought. This puts a considerable limit upon the actions to be put forth for the sake of avoiding the genetic Apocalypse (which, if a correct prediction, belongs only to the *contents* of the science of genetics). Still this is not a sufficient substance for the morality of action, or at least not all the substance a Christian will find to be valid. One who intends the world as a Christian will know man's dignity consists not only in thought or in his freedom, and he will find more elements in the nature of man to be deserving of respect and to be withheld from human handling or trespass. Specifically in connection with genetic proposals,

[47] 'Ethics in International Relations Today', an Address delivered at Amherst College, December 9, 1964. *The New York Times*, Dec. 10, 1964.

he will know that there are more ways to violate man-womanhood than to violate the *freedom* of the parties; and that something voluntarily adopted can still be wrong. He will pay attention to this as he goes about using indifferent, permitted or not immoral means to secure the *relatively* imperative ends of genetic control or improvement. To this ethics of means we turn in the next section.

In relation to genetic proposals, the most important element of Christian morality, and the most important ingredient that the Christian acknowledges to be deserving of respect in the nature of man, which needs to be brought into view is the teaching concerning *the union between* the two goods of human sexuality.

An act of sexual intercourse is at the same time an act of love and a procreative act. This does not mean that sexual intercourse always in fact nourishes love between the parties or always engenders a child. It simply means that it *tends*, of its own nature, toward the strengthening of love (the unitive good) and toward the engendering of children (the procreative good). This will be the nature of human sexual relations, provided there is no obstruction to the realization of these natural ends (for example, infertility preventing procreation or an infirm, 'infertile' or incurving heart that prevents the strengthening of the bonds of love).

Now, there has been much debate between Protestants and Roman Catholics concerning whether the unitive or the procreative good is primary or secondary, or concerning the hierarchial order or value-rank to be assigned these goods. I have shown elsewhere[48] that, contrary to popular belief, there is

[48] 'A Christian Approach to the Question of Sexual Relations Outside Marriage', in *The Journal of Religion*, XLV, 2 (April, 1965), pp. 100–118.

in the present day little or no essential difference between Roman Catholic and Protestant teachings on this point. The crucial question that remains is whether sexual intercourse as an act of love should ever be separated from sexual intercourse as a procreative act. This question remains to be decided, even if the unitive and procreative goods are equal in primacy, and even if it be said that the unitive end is the higher one. It still has to be asked, Ought men and women ever to put entirely asunder what God joined together in the mystery of our being human? Assign to sexual intercourse as an act of personal love the supreme importance, and there still remains the question whether, in what sense and in what manner this should ever be divorced from sexual intercourse as in and of itself procreative.

Now, I will state as a premise of the following discussion that an ethics (whether proposed by nominal 'Christians' or not) that *in principle* sunders these two goods – regarding procreation as an aspect of biological nature to be subjected merely to the requirements of *technical* control while saying that the unitive purpose is the free, human personal end of the matter – pays disrespect to the nature of human parenthood which does not belong among the animals God gave Adam complete *dominion* over. Such a viewpoint falls out of the bounds of the variety of Christian positions that may be taken up and debated among people who undertake to intend the world as Christians.

Still it is important that these outer limits be carefully defined in order for us to see clearly the requirements of respect for the created nature of man-womanhood, and for us not to rule out certain actions that have traditionally been excluded. Most Protestants endorse contraceptive appliances which separate while it is being exercised the sex *act* as an act of love from whatever tendency there may be in the act at the time and in the sexual powers of the parties toward the engendering of a child. But they do *not* separate the sphere or realm of their personal love from the sphere or realm of their procreation, nor between the person with whom the bond of love is nourished and the person with whom procreation may be brought into exercise. One has only to distinguish what is done in particular *acts* from what is intended and done in a whole series of acts of conjugal intercourse in order to see clearly that contraception need not exhibit an attack upon what God joined together in the creation of man-womanhood. Where 'planned parenthood' is not 'planned *un*parenthood', clearly the husband and wife do not tear their own one-flesh unity completely away from all positive response and obedience to the mystery of procreation by which it is given them in a later moment of their own union also to pass, or to intend to pass, into the one flesh of a child.

Moreover, the fact that God joined together love and progeny or the unitive and procreative purposes of sex and marriage is held in honor, and not torn asunder, even when a couple for grave or for what in their case is to them sufficient reason adopt a *life-long* policy of planned *un*parenthood. This possibility can no more be excluded by Protestant ethics than it is by Roman Catholic ethics, which teaches that under certain circumstances a couple may adopt a systematic and possibly lifelong policy of restricting their use of the unitive good to only such times as, it is believed, there is no tendency in the woman's sexual nature toward conception. The 'grave reasons' permitting this, or obliging to this, have been extended in recent years from extreme danger to the life of the woman if she attempts to give birth to include grave family financial difficulties (because the end is the procreation *and education* of the child) and even to allow that the economy of the environing society and world overpopulation may be taken into account by even the healthy and the wealthy as sufficient reason for having fewer children or for having no more at all.[49] Once mankind's genetic dilemma is called to the attention of the mind of the Church and its moral

[49] Gerald Kelley and John C. Ford, 'Periodic Continence', in *Theological Studies*, XXIII, 4 (Dec., 1962), pp. 590–624.

theologians, I see no *intrinsic* reason why these categories of analysis may not be applied to allow ample room for voluntary eugenic decisions to be made, either to have no children or to have fewer children, for the sake of future generations.

After all, Christian teachings have always held that procreation is the place where one has to perform his duty to the future of the human species; this has not been a matter of the selfish gratification of would-be parents. If the fact-situation disclosed by the science of genetics can prove that a given person cannot be the progenitor of healthy individuals, or at least not unduly defective individuals, in the next generations, then such a person's 'right to have children' becomes his duty not to do so, or to have fewer children than he might want (since he never had *any* right to have children simply for his own sake). Protestant and Roman Catholic couples in practicing eugenic control over their own reproduction may (unless the latter church changes its teaching about contraception in the wake of the Vatican Council) continue to say to one another: you in your way, and I in God's! Still, without much if any alteration of the ethical concepts currently approved, the Roman Catholic no less than the Protestant Christian could adopt a policy of lifelong non-parenthood, or less parentage, for eugenic reasons. Such married partners would still be saying by their actions that *if* either had a child, or that if either has more children, this will be from their own one-flesh unity and not apart from this. Their response to what God joined together, and to the claim He placed upon human life when He ordained that procreation come from sexual love, would be expressed by their resolve to hold acts of procreation (even the procreation they have not, or have no more) within the sphere of acts of conjugal love.

Before going on to explore the implications of Christian ethics for methods of genetic control other than the voluntary, eugenically directed birth control, it may be important to correct a misinterpretation of the principle we are using (the union of conjugal love with procreation) and to show how cardinal a principle this is in theological ethics and in the way Christians understand the entire realm with which genetics deals. It might be supposed that the moral judgments defining the outer limits of responsible human conduct are based on a mere fact of biological life, on the 'natural law' in this sense, on *Genesis*, or – as theologians would say – on the First Article of the Creed which speaks of 'creation' and the Creator. It is true that a Christian will refuse to place man's own sexual nature in the class of the animals over which Adam was given unlimited *dominion*. He will regard man as the body of his soul as well as the soul of his body, and he is not apt to locate the *humanum* of man in thought or freedom alone. He will also discern immediately that many prevalent modern views are based on other 'myths of creation'. Confronted by proposals that elevate personal freedom in the expression of procreation, and which do not honor this connection but which instead call upon men and women to act as if anything that technically can be done to exert dominion over procreation may or should be done if only it is voluntary and desirable in terms of consequences, a Christian is apt to sum them all up in a 'myth of creation' that is not his, namely, by rewriting *Genesis* to tell of the creation of man-womanhood with two separate faculties: sex serving the single end of manifesting and deepening the unity of life between the partners, while human offspring are born from the woman's brow and somehow impregnated through the ear by a cool, deliberate act of man's rational will.

Still all this would be a misunderstanding of the honor and obedience the creature should render to his Creator, and of the source of a Christian's knowledge of this. This arises not from slavish obeisance to a fact of nature. The Prologue of John's Gospel (not *Genesis*) is the Christian story of creation which provides the source and standard for responsible procreation, even as Ephesians 5 contains the ultimate reference for the meaning and nature of conjugal love. Since these two passages point to one and the same Lord – the lord over procreation as well as the lord of all marital covenants – the two aspects of human sexuality belong together, not because this is found to be the case in human and other animal bisexual reproduction.

It was out of His love that God created the entire world of His creatures. The self same love which in Ephesians 5 becomes the measure of how husbands should love their wives was, according to the Prologue, with God before all creation, and without Jesus Christ was not anything made that was made. Of course, we cannot see into the mystery of how God's love created the world. No more can we completely subdue the mystery, which is but a reflection of this, contained in the fact that human acts of love are also procreative, or why this was made to be so, in contrast to the must more 'rational' myth we constructed a moment ago. Nevertheless, we procreate new beings like ourselves in the midst of our love for one another, and in this there is a trace of the original mystery by which God created the world because of His love. God created nothing apart from His love; and without the divine love was not anything made that was made. Neither should there be among men and women, whose man-womanhood (and not their minds or wills only) is in the image of God, any love set out of the context of responsibility for procreation or any begetting apart from the sphere of love. There is a reflection of God's love binding himself to the world and the world to himself to be found in the claim He placed upon men and women in their creation when He bound the nurturing of marital love and procreation together in the nature of human sexuality. Thus, the Christian understanding of life stems from the Second Article of the Creed, not from the First or from facts of nature; and this is the source of the Christian knowledge that men and women should not put radically asunder what God joined together in creation. Thus, a Christian as such intends the world as God intends the world. We men are given to know this at the very center of the Christian faith and revelation, and here 'right' and righteousness are defined in terms of aligning our wills with His.

Men and women are created in covenant, to covenant and for covenant. Creation is *toward* the love of Christ.[50] Christians, therefore will not readily admit that the energies of sex, for example, have any other primary *telos*, another final end, than Jesus Christ. They will rather find in the strength of human sexual passion, beyond the obvious needs of procreation, an evident *telos* of acts of sexual love toward making real the meaning of man-womanhood, nurturing covenant-love between the parties, fostering their care for one another, prefiguring Christ's love for the Church – whatever other sub-strata of purposes sexual energy may have as this can be discovered by intending the world as a biologist. And in human procreativity out of the depths of human sexual love is prefigured God's own act of creation out of the profound mystery of his love revealed in Christ. To put radically asunder what God joined together in parenthood when He made love procreative, to procreate from beyond the sphere of love (AID, for example, or making human life in a test-tube) or to posit acts of sexual love beyond

[50] In these and other statements in the explanation in the text above, I may seem no longer to be within hailing distance of normative Judaism, or of what follows from intending the world as a Jew. There is a profound, *formal* analogy, however, to be taken into account if anyone wants to understand the basic theological ethics that is or should be controlling in the specific teachings of Judaism. Normative Judaism, or at least the theology of the Jewish Scriptures, also understand creation from the point of view of covenant. From the center of those events in which God created a negligible people to be His people, they understand his will in creating anything else out of "nothing," covenanting with the sun and moon and stars. And from the point of view of God's faithfulness they interpret the fidelity or steadfastness manifest anywhere in the world, while depending on God's Messiah more than on anything else to prove it.

the sphere of responsible procreation (by definition, marriage), means a refusal of the image of God's creation in our own.

A science-based culture, such as the present one, of necessity erodes and makes nonsense out of all sorts of bonds and connections which a Christian sees to be the case. Thus, because of its atomistic individualism, modern thought delivers the verdict 'guilty of *monopoly*' upon the definition of marriage as a mutual and exclusive exchange of right to acts which of themselves tend to the nurturing of love or unity of life and to the engendering of children – when all that was meant by these words is that there is a bond of life with life. And among geneticists, H.J. Muller, for one, delivers the verdict guilty of 'genetic proprietorship that so many men hold dear' or 'fixation on the attempted perpetuation of just his own particular genes',[51] and 'feelings of proprietary rights and prerogatives about one's own germinal material, supported by misplaced egotism'[52] – when all that is at stake in the historic ethics of the western world and actually in the minds of a great many people today is the bond to be held in respect between personal love and procreation, which, as explained above, is about as far from selfish proprietorship as anything can be, and as far as marriage is from monopoly. There may be an irrepressible conflict between the values governing in some genetic proposals and the historic values expressed by Christians, but there is no reason for the conflict to be an irrational one, or irrationally conceived. This happens today wherever there is evidently such an unparalleled breakdown of our moral tradition that men of science cannot even understand what is being said in the utterance of Christian ethical judgments. The verdicts 'monopoly' and 'proprietorship over germinal material' turn into judgments upon a whole

[51] H.J. Muller, 'Means and Ends in Human Genetic Betterment', in T.M. Sonneborn, *op. cit.*

[52] H.J. Muller, 'The Guidance of Human Evolution', in *Perspectives in Biology and Medicine*, p. 26.

culture that produces great intelligences capable of uttering them, or incapable of understanding Christian ethics except in terms of these absurdities.[53]

In the preceding paragraphs I have attempted to explain the substance of that 'ethics of means' which Christianity adds to the insistence of scientific humanism upon the use only of voluntary means in any program of genetic control. I have tried to express what morally is at stake for the Christian religious ethics, and the rationale it lays down for determining the nature and limits of specifiably legitimate conduct in this area. We have now to resume our examination of the various methods that have been proposed for the control or improvement of man's genetic inheritance, evaluating these in the light of the requirement that there be no complete or radical or 'in principle'

[53] 'One must face the fact that there is eventually bound to be a conflict of values,' said Crick in the discussion in *Man and His Future*, p. 380. 'It is hopeful that at the moment we can get a measure of agreement, but I think that in time the facts of science are going to make us become less Christian.' The subject of this discerning remark was the disagreement between Christians, with 'their particular prejudice about the sanctity of the individual', and those who 'simply want to try it scientifically' (whom, strangely, Crick called 'humanists'!). But when it came to any of the finer points, such as those discussed in the text above, which anyone who presumes at all to take up the subject of Christian ethics makes himself responsible for knowing, Crick could only use a very blunt and unanalysed notion of people's 'right to have children' which, he asserted, is 'taken for granted because it is a part of Christian ethics'. Against this supposed notion, he wanted to 'get across to people the idea that their children are not entirely [*sic*] their own business and that it is not a private matter' (*Ibid.*, p. 275). And in the discussion in Hoagland and Burhoe, *op. cit.* Professor D. H. Fleming, historian at Harvard, expressed some degree of reluctance to have science assume the moral leadership of mankind by adopting Muller's proposals, because, he said, this would 'represent a passing over to science of the traditional role of religion as the fountainhead of restraints upon pleasurable conduct' (p. 65). To which the appropriate reply is: 'Goshallhemlock!'

separation between the personally unitive and the procreative aspects of human sexual life. By this standard there would seem to be no objection to eugenically motivated birth control if the facts are sufficient to show that genetic defects belong among those grave reasons that may warrant the systematic or even lifelong prevention of conception. A husband and wife who decide to practice birth control for eugenic reasons are still resolved to hold acts of procreation (even the procreation they have not, or have no more) within the sphere of conjugal love.

This understanding of the moral limits upon methods that may properly be adopted in voluntary genetic control leads also, I would argue, to the permissability of artificial conception control no less than the so-called rhythm method, and to the endorsement of voluntary sterilization for eugenic reasons. I know that many of my fellow Christians do not agree with these conclusions. Yet it seems clear that both are open for choice as means (if the ends are important enough), provided Christian ethics is no longer restricted to the analysis of individual *acts* and instead is concerned with the coincidence of the *spheres* of personal sexual love and of procreation to which particular actions belong. Neither people who practice artificial birth control nor a husband who decides to have vasectomy are saying by the total course of their lives anything other than that *if* either has a child, or has more children, this will be from their own one-flesh unity and not apart from this. In principle, they hold together, they do not put completely asunder, what God joined together – the sphere of procreation, even the procreation they have not or have no more, and the sphere where they exchange acts that nurture their unity of life with one another. They honor the union between love and creation at the heart of God's act toward the world of his creatures, and the image of this in the union of love with procreativity in their own man-womanhood. Their morality is not oriented upon the genetic consequences alone which are believed to justify *any* voluntary means; nor is it an ethic of inner intention alone which is believed to make any sort of conduct right. They *do* something, and are constantly engaged in doing it, which gives their behavior a character that is derived neither wholly from the desired results nor from subjective intention. They actually unite through a whole course of life their loving and their procreativity (which, incidental to this, they have not). So they do not do wrong. They do no wrong that good may come of it. They do right that good may come of it. (In this moral reasoning, the present writer can see no difference between the case for contraception and the case for voluntary contraceptive sterilization, except in not unimportant differences in the findings of fact that may warrant the one or the other, and the fact that as yet sterilization is ordinarily irreversible. And even in terms of the more static formulations of the past, it should certainly be said that a vasectomy may be a far less serious invasion of nature than massive assault upon the woman's generative organism by means of contraceptive pills.)

I am aware that many Christians will not agree with these conclusions – and that others than Roman Catholics will be in disagreement. I ask the latter simply to consider the following possible development in the basic structure of their own ethical analysis of these problems. Suppose that in the near future Roman Catholic teachings effect the shift from act-analysis (from concentrating upon features of *the act* of conjugal intercourse that ought not to be put asunder) to concentration upon these same features within the order of marriage, the sphere or realm of marriage, that ought not to be radically separated. This, I predict, will be the theological-ethical grounds for any approval of the use of contraceptive devices in acts or in a series of acts of conjugal intercourse, if Catholic teachings make this advance. It will not be by reference to the indirect effects of the pill upon regularizing the woman's menstrual cycle: if only the pill is approved, that will show the continued sway of act-analysis upon

Catholic teachings. But if the order of marriage comes to the fore in Catholic moral reasoning, with the goods that should be held together between the parties, that will warrant artificial contraception generally, where there is sufficient reason for controlling reproduction.

If this is the step taken, it seems to me impossible to avoid the conclusion that voluntary male sterilization (when this is ordinarily a reversible operation) will find a place among the means of contraception, perhaps preferable to other means that might be chosen. Then, if there are reasons for the systematic and lifelong practice of birth control (already a conclusion reached by Catholic moral theology) and if serious genetic defect finds a place among the reasons grave enough to warrant having no children at all, or no more at all, then vasectomy would seem to be in principle permissable, perhaps commendable, maybe morally obligatory. Finally, where there is sufficiently grave reason for systematic, lifelong birth control, Christian moral reflection need not wait on the assured reversibility of vasectomy in order to reach an affirmative conclusion upon this question. All this follows in the wake of taking quite seriously what I have tried to suggest by saying that a man and a woman do not set creation asunder or disobey their Creator's will when they honor the union of their love with their procreativity, even the procreativity they have not, or have no more, within the bond of marriage they hold between them. They do not procreate from beyond their marriage, or exercise love's one-flesh unity elsewhere.

The notation to be made concerning 'genetic surgery', or the introduction of some anti-mutagent chemical intermediary, which will eliminate a genetic defect before it can be passed on through reproduction, is simple. Should the practice of such medical genetics become feasible at some time in the future it will raise no moral questions at all – or at least none that are not already present in the practice of medicine generally. Morally, medical genetics to enable a man and a woman to be able to engender a child without some defective gene they have been discovered to carry would seem to be on all fours with treatment to cure infertility if one of the partners bears this defect. Any significant difference arises from the vastly greater complexity of the practice of genetic surgery and the seriousness of the consequences if because of insufficient knowledge an error is made. The cautionary word to be applied here is simply the moral warning against culpable ignorance. The science of genetics and medical practice based on it would be obliged to be fully informed of the facts and it should have a reasonable and well-examined expectation of doing more good than harm by eliminating the genetic defect in question. The seriousness of this consideration arises from the serious matter with which genetic surgery will be dealing. Still the culpability of actions put forth in removable ignorance cannot be invoked as a caution without allowing, at the same time, that in the practice of genetic medicine there doubtless will be errors made in inculpable ignorance. But genetic injuries of this order would be *tragic*, like birth injuries under certain circumstances. They would not entail *wrong*-doing; nor should applications of genetic science be stopped until all such eventualities are impossible. That would be an impossible demand, which no morality imposes.

The paradox is that the most unquestionably moral means of genetic control (direct action upon the genotype by some 'surgical' or chemical anti-mutagent before it is produced) is technically the most difficult and distant in the future;[54] while

[54] H.J. Muller, who favors phenotypic selection, describes the enormous difficulties in the way of perfecting methods of genotypic change in 'Means and Aims in Human Betterment', in T.M. Sonneborn, *op. cit.* In the advancement of science toward the direction or change of the germ cells themselves, Muller believes 'there may be in time a race between genetic surgery and robotics, and we may find that "this old house will do no longer".' I take him to mean that a new type of man may be as easily made

a number of the means presently available (phenotypic breeding in or breeding out) are of quite questionable morality, and questionable for reasons that the voluntariness of the practice would not remove.

In the foregoing an affirmative notation has been placed beside genetically motivated conception control and voluntary sterilization. Before going on to other methods of achieving 'empirical', genotypic or parental selection beside which a negative notation must be placed, let a moralist confess himself to be in a quandary after reading some of the scientific literature concerning the paradox just mentioned. Some geneticists stress the great strides that could be taken toward solving mankind's genetic dilemma if science achieves the competence to perform genetic surgery and to direct mutation, or back mutation. These point out how little could be accomplished by empirical parent selection, short of forcing the gene pool of the future through a very narrow corridor and by compulsion bringing about the genetic extinction of a great number of potential reproducers.[55] Other geneticists stress what can be achieved in negative or positive eugenics by the voluntary use of the means of germinal selection at present available. These point out how almost unimaginably difficult and distant – and by comparison, roundabout and unnecessary – is the perfection of genetic surgery.

as present man can be remade by direct action on his genes. Neither, for Muller, is 'utterly visionary'. Since both robotics and the direction of mutation are, however, visionary, Muller wants to proceed with parental selection by all the voluntary means presently available.

[55] Michael Lerner, Professor of Genetics at the University of California (Berkeley), pointed out that animal breeders made little improvement until they 'had clearly defined objectives', 'used exceedingly high levels of inbreeding – the basis of breed fixation', and used 'very expensive techniques in terms of genetic extinction, that is, in terms of preventing the reproduction of huge numbers of individuals in order to improve the trait of one or two percent' (in the discussion in Hoagland and Burhoe, *op. cit.*, p. 55).

Here is a conflict of scientific judgments, and one which may entail a subtle and suppressed moral judgment among geneticists themselves leading to the difference in their reading of the fact-situation and in prognosis. In any case, it is quite impossible for a moralist who is a non-scientist to make his way to an analysis that he is confident is soundly based. This may give him the freedom to reach moral conclusions in his own right. Nevertheless, a layman cannot know which opinion to endorse, nor whether there is an emerging consensus among geneticists, nor whether the disagreement is wholly scientific or partly moral, when confronted by the following, opposing statements:

(1) '...The technology of human genetics is pitifully clumsy, even by the standards of practical agriculture. Surely within a few generations we can expect to learn tricks of immeasurable advantage. *Why bother now with somatic selection, so slow in its impact?*'[56]

(2) 'It is preposterous to suppose that, in the foreseeable future, knowledge would be precise enough to enable us to say what substitution to make in order to effect a given, desired phenotypic alteration... But to suppose that, after it had become possible, men would still be bound by the reproductive traditions of today, *preferring this ultra-sophisticated method of improvement to the readily available one* of selecting donor material free from the given defect or already possessing the desired innovation – that would be a calumny on the rationality of the human race. It would be like supposing that in some technically advanced society elaborate superhighways were constructed to carry vehicles *on enormous detours* to avoid defiling hallowed domains reserved in perpetuity for their millions of sacred cows.'[57]

I must say that this last quotation from H.J. Muller indicates

[56] Joshua Lederberg, 'Biological Future of Man', in *Man and His Future*, p. 265 (italics added).

[57] H.J. Muller, 'The Guidance of Human Evolution', in *Perspectives in Biology and Medicine*, p. 37 (italics added).

that he may be sorely in need of instruction in the difference between 'sacred cows' and that 'sacredness in the temporal order' who is *man*. Muller, of course, respects man's quality as a thinking animal; he would not violate his freedom, and he challenges men to noble action. This ethics, we have pointed out, is not to be found among the contents of the science of genetics, but is rather the necessary presupposition of man the geneticist and the fruit of intending the world with a scientific mind or else Muller's humanism is a fruit of intending the world as a man within the community of men. Neither is Christian ethics to be found among the contents of any natural science, nor can it be disproven by any of the facts that such sciences know. It is a fruit of intending the world as a Christian. (Here is no conflict between religion and science, but a conflict between two philosophies.) The Christian understands the *humanum* of man to include the body of his soul no less than the soul (mind) of his body. In particular, he holds in honor the union of the realm of personal love with the realm of procreativity in man-womanhood, which is the image of God's creation in the midst of His love. Since artificial insemination by means of semen from a non-husband donor (AID) puts completely asunder what God joined together, this proposed method of genetic control or genetic improvement must be defined as an exercise of illicit dominion over man no less than would be the case if his free will is forced. Not all dominion over man's own physical nature, of course, is wrong, but *this* would be – for the reasons stated above.

In outline, Muller proposes that 'germinal choice' be secured by giving eugenic direction to AID (Julian Huxley called this 'pre-adoption'), which has already become a minority 'institution' in our society; and that comparable techniques be developed and employed: 'foster pregnancy' and parthenogenesis (or stimulated asexual reproduction). Moreover, just as the enormous difficulties in the way of perfecting punctiform genetic surgery or mutational direction by chemical intermediaries impel Muller to concentrate attention on presently available techniques of parental selection, so the apparently small gains for the race that can be secured by negative eugenics (because the genes will continue in great numbers as recessives or in heterozygotes) impel him on to the advocacy of positive or progressive eugenics.[58] In this, one does not have to identify the genetic defects, or know that they do not add vigor in hybrids. One has only to identify the desired genotype (itself no small problem!) and breed for this.

Instead of choosing a donor who is likely to engender a child resembling the 'adopting' father, instead of using medical students (notoriously not of the highest intelligence) or bar-hops, instead of using AID only when the husband is infertile or the carrier of grave genetic defect, and instead of keeping the matter secret, Muller proposes the selection of donors of the highest, proven physical, mental, emotional and moral traits and that publicity be given to the practice so that more and more people may follow our genetic leaders and voluntarily decide to bestow upon their 'children' the very best genetic inheritance instead of their own precious genes.

In order for this to be done most effectively, Muller proposes that a system of deep-frozen semen banks be established and that records of phenotypes be kept and evaluated. At least twenty years should be allowed to elapse before the frozen semen is used, in order for a sound judgment to be made upon the donor's capacities. The men who earn enduring esteem can thus be 'manifolded' and 'called upon to reappear age after age

[58] 'As in most defensive operations, it is dreary, frustrating business to have to run as fast as one can merely to stay in the same place. Nature did better for us. What can we not do better for ourselves?' ('The Guidance of Human Evolution', in *Perspectives in Biology and Medicine*, p. 17). Thus, only progressive eugenics would be the equivalent of natural selection, which was phenotypic and preserved the genes of the strongest types.

until the population in general had caught up with them.'[59] It is an insufficient answer to this to point out[60] that in his 1935 book, *Out of the Night*, Muller believed that no intelligent and morally sensitive woman would refuse to bear a child of Lenin, while in later versions Lenin is omitted and Einstein, Pasteur, Descartes, Leonardo and Lincoln are nominated. Muller might well reply either by defending Lenin or by saying that not enough time had elapsed for him to know.

To his fellow geneticists can be left the task of stating and demonstrating scientific and other socio-psychological objections – which include the fact that the genes of a supposedly superior male may contain injurious recessives which by artificial insemination would become widespread throughout the population instead of remaining in small proportion, as they now do;[61] that the children of geniuses now alive do not give too much support to this proposal; that 'it might turn out that parents who looked forward eagerly to having a Horowitz in the family would discover later that it was not so fine as they expected because he might have a temperament incompatible with that of a normal family'; that 'it is bad enough if we take responsibility only for the environment of our children; if we take responsibility for their genetic make-up, too, the guilt may become unbearable';[62] that we know nothing about the mutation rate that would continue in the frozen germ cells; that the IQ's of criminals would be raised;[63] that we could not have a 'healthy society' because not many men would be 'emotionally satisfied

[59] 'The Guidance of Human Evolution', in *Perspectives in Biology and Medicine*, p. 35.

[60] Th. Dobshansky, *op. cit.*, p. 328; and Klein's comment in the discussion in *Man and His Future*, p. 280.

[61] J. Paul Scott in the discussion in Hoagland and Burhoe, *op. cit.*, p. 48.

[62] R. S. Morison in *ibid.*, p. 64.

[63] Donald M. MacKay in the discussion in *Man and His Future*, *op. cit.*, p. 298.

by children not their own.'[64] Without opening these questions, my verdict has been negative, in terms of the morality of means which Christian ethics must use as its standard of judgment.[65]

However, a word more should be said. No disciplined analysis of the moral life should fail to say that, among wrong actions, some are wronger than others. For the Roman Catholic, for example, abortion is worse than artificial conception control; and among invasions of man's generative faculties, some are more serious than others. While Muller's proposals would constitute a very serious invasion and an utter separation of the realm of procreation from the realm of conjugal love, it might be that, upon serious reflection upon the genetic problem, a Christian moralist could reach the conclusion that the genetic motivation and probable consequences of Muller's AID would add to it a redeeming feature, without, however, this being sufficient to place the practice in the class of *morally permitted* actions.

Moreover, the judgment that AID for genetic or any other purposes is morally wrong does not entail the conclusion that it should be prohibited by law. Not all 'sin' should be defined as a 'crime'. Not all immoral conduct is a fit subject for prohibitive legislation, but only acts that seriously affect the common good. It can be seriously debated whether one of a number of current opinions concerning AID touches the common good so deeply that it belongs in the class of those immoral practices which should also be declared illegal. It is true that AID touches the

[64] John F. Brock in *ibid.*, p. 287. Or that, in view of the incredible diversity of opinions expressed by the scientists, it is impossible to know what to try to educate people to do in making genetic choices (Medawar in *ibid.*, p. 382).

[65] There is an exceedingly profound and open-minded discussion of artificial insemination, from the point of view of a Lutheran ethics, to be found in Helmut Thielicke's *The Ethics of Sex*. New York, Harper and Row, 1964, pp. 248–268.

moral nature of human parenthood (and tries to define this in terms of what it is not) just as deeply – Roman Catholics believe – as legal divorce touches the nature of marriage (and attempts to define this contrary to its nature). Still Roman Catholics do not always and everywhere teach that under no circumstances should there be legislation permitting and regulating 'divorce' (which for them is morally impossible); and when this conclusion is reached it is by making a distinction between 'sin' and 'crime', or between conduct which is or is not a fit subject for prohibitive legislation which must be ever watchful to mold the common good out of the actual ethos of the people whose affairs it regulates. AID is an area in which Anglo-American law fairly bristles with contradictions which will soon have to be cleared up one way or another, by prohibitory or permissive and regulatory legislation or by case law. I am suggesting that it may be possible to justify the legal enactment of AID without basing this on its moral justification.[66] If so – or if in any case this is the cumulative judgment our society is making – then I suppose that a trial can and will be made to see what can be accomplished eugenically by education and action in accord with Muller's proposals.

Finally, it ought to be pointed out that the practice of freezing and storing sperm cells has a possibly desirable connection with genetically motivated voluntary sterilization. As a complement of vasectomy, this would provide germinal insurance that may have some role to play, unless and until vasectomy becomes ordinarily a reversible operation, in encouraging men with moderately serious genetic defects to limit their offspring. Germinal insurance would fall within the genetic decisions of

[66] The Roman Catholic legal authority, Norman St. John-Stevas, *Life, Death and the Law*. Bloomington, Indiana: Indiana University Press, 1961, pp. 116–159, gives a good account of the theological, moral and legal aspects of this question. He leans in the opposite direction from the position suggested in the text above.

persons who, in adopting voluntary contraceptive sterilization for eugenic reasons, are still resolved to hold together the realm of sexual love and the realm of procreation in the acts of sexual intercourse they exercise.

Finally, we need to bring under scrutiny the ends or objectives of genetic control, and the choice to be made between negative eugenics (by breeding-out or by back-mutation) and progressive eugenics (by breeding-in or by the positive direction of mutation).

H.J. Muller has supreme confidence that those pioneering spirits who lead the way in this generation in the employment of germinal selection can be trusted to choose, from among a variety of choiceworthy genotypes described to them by the keepers of the semen banks, the types that will be good for mankind to produce in greater numbers. 'Can these critics', he asks, 'really believe that the persons of unusual moral courage, progressive spirit, and eagerness to serve mankind, who will pioneer in germinal choice, and likewise those who in a more enlightened age will follow in the path thus laid down, will fail to recognize the fundamental human values...?'[67] It is true, Muller expresses the guiding aims of particular eugenic decisions in quite general terms: 'practically all peoples', he writes, 'venerate creativity, wisdom, brotherliness, loving-kindness, perceptivity, expressivity, joy of life, fortitude, vigour, longevity.'[68] Or again: '...What is meant by superior is whatever is conducive to greater wisdom, cooperativeness, happiness, harmony of nature, or richness of potentialities.'[69] This under-

[67] H.J. Muller, 'Better Genes fro Tomorrow', in Stuart Mudd, ed.: *The Population Crisis and the Use of World Resoirces*. Dr W. Junk Publishers, The Hague, 1964, p. 336.

[68] H.J. Muller, 'Genetic Progress by Voluntarily Conducted Germinal Choice', in *Man and His Future*, p. 260.

[69] H.J. Muller, 'The World View of Moderns', a Lecture, University of Illinois Press, 1958, p. 26. Without some consensus on the ultimate question

standing of the goals of eugenic decisions may be open to the objection that, in animal husbandry, one has to have very narrowly defined criteria governing the selection to be made. It is less open to the objection stated by Th. Dobzhansky: 'Muller's implied assumption that there is, or can be, *the* ideal human genotype which it is desirable to bestow upon everybody is not only unappealing but almost certainly wrong – it is human diversity that acted as a leaven of creative effort in the past and will so act in the future.'[7]- There is range enough, it would seem, in Muller's description of ideal man to permit a great variety of specific genotypes. The fact is that within these very general value assumptions, Muller counts on specific couples to pick the specific genotype they want to bestow on their 'preadoptive' children.[71] 'Couples so enlightened as to resort in this and the next generation to germinal choice will not require a corps of axiologists or sociologists to tell them what are the most crying genetic needs of the man of today.'[72] Thus, Muller is confident that a host of particular choices made by people who have concrete options presented to them can be laid, as it were, end to end with similar choices made by people in succeeding generations, whose choices will doubtless improve as their genetic inheritance improves, to produce a continuity of choices

of values, he points out, all man's cultural activities, no less than germinal choices, would be at cross-purposes. 'The Guidance of Human Evolution' in *Perspectives in Biology and Medicine*, p. 19.

[70] Th. Dobzhansky, *op. cit.*, p. 330.

[71] '...Couples desiring to have in their own families one or more children who are especially likely to embody their own ideals of worth will be afforded a wide range of choice. They will be assisted by records of the lives and characteristics of the donors and of their relatives, and by counsel from diverse specialists, but the final choice will be their own and their participation will be entirely voluntary.' H.J. Muller, 'Means and Aims in Human Genetic Betterment', in T.M. Sonneborn, *op. cit.*

[72] *Ibid.*

in the ascending direction of genetic improvement, which was formerly the work of natural selection. This hope is only exceeded by Muller's certainty that, unless man assumes the direction of his genetic goals, the descent of the species is the sole alternative expectation.

Place beside this the objection Donald M. Mackay raised based on the fact that the generation that first initiates genetic control cannot determine the goals that will be set by future generations – or establish any directional continuity. No one can prevent 'the "goal-setting" from drifting and oscillating as time goes on, under the influence of external or even internal factors.' Suppose genotype X is chosen in a majority of instances in the first generation. No one can know 'what kind of changes these men of type X would think desirable in their successors – and so on, into the future.' If we cannot answer this question and *establish* a continuity from the beginning, then 'to initiate such a process might show the reverse of responsibility, on any explication of the term.' (Moreover, unless this question is answered and unless future answers to it are assured, then the process would be quite unlike animal husbandry.) 'In short, to navigate by a landmark tied to your own ship's head is ultimately impossible.'[73]

Now, how does one adjudicate between these opposing views? It is obvious that these judgments fall far outside the science of genetics itself. There may even be operative of kind of ultimate determination of one man's individual mode of being in the world toward making man the creator and determiner of his own evolution and on the part of the other scientist a personal determination away from this dizzy prospect. The present writer would say that one has to be a rather thoroughgoing relativist who denies to man any fundamental competence to make moral judgments to refuse to concede some degree of truth to Muller's opinion. This is why, in addition to genetically motivated conception control and voluntary sterilization, I have

[73] Donald M. MacKay in the discussion in *Man and His Future*, p. 286.

conceded that, if AID is not to be prohibited by law, it might morally be a better wrong with the intent to bestow a better genetic inheritance upon such a child than if done with complete anonimity with regard to the donor's genotypic qualities and only for the sake of securing a child as much like the putative parents as possible. In any case, the voluntariness of the genetic decisions made in any one generation and through the generations insures the *usus* of Muller's proposal against such *abusus* as would forbid it *from the point of view of the ends only*, and would seem to render somewhat inconsequential such oscillation in goalsetting as might take place. Such oscillation in genetic decisions would be roughly comparable to oscillations in cultural decisions (taking place under the guidance of Muller's *jus gentium*) that may occur over the sweep of centuries; and the one would be no more and no less consequential than the other, while reciprocating strength to the other.

On the other side of this question, it must be acknowledged that this way of characterizing the goals to be set for positive human betterment do, despite their generality, describe the characteristics of a good geneticist or the virtues of a good community of scientists or, at least, the special values of man in the contemporary period. This is a science-based age, and an age of rapid social change in which men dream of inhabiting other planets after dispoiling this one. It is an age in which 'progressives' are in the saddle and ride mankind – ahead if not forward. In such an age it is natural enough that most of man's problems are defined in terms of 'social lag' of one sort or another, and in terms of the laggard type of characters our genes continue to produce. Still in the long view mankind might be in the greatest peril if it succeeded in finding a way to increase its own momentum, by selecting on a large scale for the special values of this present culture. In the long view, the race may have need of laggard types and traditional societies, who could take up the history of humanity again after the breakdown of the more momentous civilizations. If positive genetics gained its way, even under the aegis of a quite unexceptionable *jus gentium* setting the goals, would this not unavoidably take the form of genetically instituting some parochial *jus civilis?*

Partly because of the difficulties concerning 'goal setting' and because the negative goals would seem to be clearer, the present writer leans in the direction of approving preventive eugenics only. This is also because the means to the ends of preventive genetics – whether these be the voluntary control of conception or anti-mutagent surgery or chemicals – seem, at our present state of knowledge, to have the good effect of eliminating bad effects without as much danger of producing also an overflow of incalculable, unintended bad consequences. We may say with Hampton L. Carlson, 'let us recommend preventive eugenics but proceed very cautiously in progressive eugenics. A firm scientific basis for the latter does not now exist.'[74]

It must be admitted that the total population effects of negative genetics may not be very effective in bringing about large scale prevention of the deterioration of the gene pool. Nevertheless, in face of such pessimistic predictions, 'it is well to remember that every defective individual that can be avoided represents a positive gain.'[75] Also, if genetics can identify the carriers of genetic defects and we no longer need restrict preventive genetics to persons who are identifiably unfit themselves, if in short a qualitative control of reproduction can wisely be adopted by, and at some time in the future back mutation can be performed helpfully upon, a larger proportion of the population, then the results of preventive eugenics need not be so limited as it has been in the past. To sterilize *forcibly* all persons themselves suffering from serious genetic defect would have hardly any influence on the proportion of that particular recessive gene in the population. But if carriers can be identified, and if

[74] Hampton L. Carlson, *op. cit.*, p. 189.

[75] *Ibid.*, p. 188.

each heterozygous carrier had only half as many children as he would otherwise have, this would reduce the abnormal-gene frequency by 50%. This alone would greatly reduce the incidence of the disease in the next generation, and prevent untold future human misery.[76]

To make preventive eugenics more effective will require the development and widespread adoption of an 'ethics of genetic duty'. It is shocking to learn, from the heredity clinics that have been established in recent years in more than a dozen cities in the United States, how many parents will accept grave risk of having defective children rather than remain childless. 'When a husband and wife each carry a recessive deleterious gene similar to the one carried by the other, the chances of their having a defective child are one in four, with two children carriers of a single gene, but themselves without defect, and [only] the fourth child being neither a carrier nor defective. Couples in such a position, knowing that they have one chance in four of having a seriously defective child, and that two out of four of their children are likely to be carriers, still frequently take a chance that things will turn out all right.'[77] This can only be called genetic imprudence, with the further notation that imprudence as such is gravely immoral.

In making genetic decisions to be put into effect by morally acceptable means, the benefits expected from a given course of action must be weighed against any risk (or loss of good) incurred. This is exactly the mode of moral reasoning used in reaching a conclusion about whether or not to use X-rays in medical diagnosis, or radiation therapy in medical treatments. Should patients with cancerous growths, for whom because of age and condition of health the expectation of parenthood is

[76] See James F. Crow, 'Mechanisms and Trends in Human Evolution', in Hoagland and Burhoe, *op. cit.*, p. 18.

[77] Frederick Osborn, 'The Protection and Improvement of Man's Genetic Inheritance', in Stuart Mudd, *op. cit.*, pp. 308–309.

quite small, be subjected to massive radiation therapy? The answer here is obviously affirmative. But how does one compare the detection of a case of tuberculosis by X-ray survey with the genetic harm that will befall someone in generations to come? How compelling should the indication be before an unborn child is subjected to damage in connection with a fluoroscopic examination of its mother?[78] Moral reasoning that applies the principle of prudence, or the principle of proportion between effects both of which arise from a single action, is notoriously inexact. Still, it is certain that it is *immoral* to be imprudent, and it is a dereliction of duty not to make this sort of appraisal as best one can, and to act upon the best knowledge one can secure.

It is hardly utopian to hope that with the dissemination of genetic knowledge there will arise increased concern about this problem, and among an increasing number of people a far greater moral sensitivity to their responsibilities to the future generations of mankind. Such an 'ethics of genetic duty' was well stated by H.J. Muller: '...Although it is a human right

[78] See Wallace and Dobzhansky, *op. cit.*, pp. 184–185.

Since these authors had just cogently stated (perhaps without knowing it) the 'rule of double effect', I frankly do not understand their meaning in the following paragraph: 'The importance one places on genetic damage depends, really, on the value one places on human life. If the importance of human life is absolute, if human life is infinitely precious, then the exact number of additional victims of genetic damage is not crucial. One death is as inadmissible as 100, 1 000, or 1 000 000. Infinity multiplied by any finite number is still infinity. Whoever claims that the number of genetic deaths is an important consideration in this problem claims that human life is of limited value.' (p. 188). To the contrary, it is precisely because each human life has such value that it becomes important to take the numbers into account as one element in the proportion in situations where *not all can be saved*. Prudence is a matter of estimating the cost-benefit where infinite values (the lives of persons) are in conflict, where, *e.g.*, persons in the present generation must be saved at the expense of persons in a future generation, or *vice versa;* and there is *no other alternative*.

for people to have their infirmities cared for by every means that society can muster, they do not have the right knowingly to pass on to posterity such a load of infirmities of genetic or partly genetic origin as to cause an increase in the burden already being carried by the population.'[79]

There is ample and well-established ground in Christian ethics for enlarging upon the theme of man's genetic responsibility. Having children was never regarded as a selfish prerogative. Instead Christian teachings have always held that procreation is the place where men and women are to perform their duty to the future of the human species. If a given couple cannot be the progenitors of healthy individuals, or at least not unduly defective individuals, or if they will be the carriers of serious defect, then such a couple's 'right to have children' becomes their duty not to do so, or to have fewer children. The science of genetics may be able to inform them with certain knowledge of the fact situation that is sufficient to place eugenic reasons among these serious causes justifying the systematic practice of lifelong *un*parenthood, or of less parentage.

What is lacking is not the moral argument but a moral movement. The Christian churches have in the past been able to promote celibacy to the glory of God, men and women who for the supreme End of human existence 'deny themselves' (if that is the word for it) both of the goods of marriage. These same Christian churches should be able to promote voluntary or 'vocational' childlessness, or policies of restricted reproduction, for the sake of the children of generations to come. In place of Muller's 'foster pregnancy', the churches could set before such couples alternatives that might be termed 'foster parentage' – all the many ways in which human parental instincts may be fulfilled in couples who for mercy's sake have no children of their

[79] H.J. Muller, 'Man's Future Birthright', a Lecture. University of New Hampshire, 1958, p. 18. See also Muller's 'The Guidance of Human Evolution', in *Perspectives in Biology and Medicine*, p. 8.

own. These persons would be called upon to 'deny themselves' (if that is the word for it) one of the goods of marriage for the sake of that end itself. And they would honor the Creator of all human love and procreation, in that they would hold in incorruptible union the love that they have and the procreation they never have, or have no more.

KINGSLEY DAVIS

Sociological aspects of genetic control

DR KINGSLEY DAVIS *was born in Texas in 1908 and graduated with honors from the University of Texas. He received his PhD degree at Harvard University in 1936, since when he has worked in the fields of sociology and population research. He is a challenging thinker on the sociology of reproduction and his stature is reflected in his election as president of the American Sociological Society in 1959 and as President of the Population Association of America in 1962. He is Professor of Sociology at the University of California at Berkeley, a title he has also held at Pennsylvania State and Columbia Universities.*

The organic world represents, as the previous chapters make clear, a compromise between stability and change. On the one hand, the segregation of the germ cells partially insulates each species from temporary environmental disturbances. On the other hand, random mutations and enduring environmental shifts gradually alter the species through natural selection.

A comparable but less recognized reconciliation of stability with change is achieved in human societies. These are composed of generations of individuals who have not only the genetic constitution and hence the biological stability of the species but also a culturally transmitted system resistant to alteration. The mechanisms by which human societies minimize social change are numerous. They include restraints on aberrant individuals, indoctrination of the young in traditions and myths, use of conservative members of the society (such as housewives) to rear the next generation, antipathy to strange customs and languages, interpretation of loyalty to the group as agreement with its ways. Such mechanisms do not preclude social change, but they slow it down. The degree of stability they achieve tends to be overlooked, because people mistake the short-run swings and shifts of their milieu for alternations of social structure. Fads and fashions, the circulation of the elite, shifts in governmental regimes – these generally have little effect on societal evolution. Indeed, descriptions of political behavior by Plato or Aristotle and accounts of family life or religious cults in stone-age cultures demonstrate how little human society has changed over thousands of years. The main changes have been in the instrumentalities. Dazzling as these may be, it is amazing to what extent they are used for human goals that have undergone little or no change.

Two principles of human improvement

Once it is granted that Homo sapiens participates in these two distinct systems of compromise between stability and change, several implications can be drawn. One inference, for example, is that attempts to improve mankind – that is, to thwart stability and maximize desired change – can deal with either system. They can alter the biological capacities and traits of the human organism by artificial selection, or they can reform the culturally transmitted institutions through social movement. Interestingly, only one of these methods – the second – has ever been tried. The genetic approach, though sometimes discussed, has never been used for human beings on a significant scale, despite its success with plants and animals.

We thus come to a puzzling scientific question. Since the two methods of human reform are not mutually exclusive, why is it that only one has been utilized? Each method rests on a distinct and effective principle. Beyond doubt the inherited make-up of a species can be altered by planned intervention. Beyond doubt a social system can be changed by deliberate effort. It follows that any proposed improvement in man's condition could theoretically be pursued by both methods at once with no conflict (unless of course the improvement excludes one or the other method by definition). For instance, those who seek to eliminate warfare in human society could seek (a) to get an international language adopted – on the assumption that differences of language lead to wars and (b) to breed individuals who are less innately aggressive – on the theory that human temper and passion lead to armed conflict. Similarly, those who wish to strengthen human health could try (a) to institute new health practices and medical services and (b) to reduce the reproduction rate among carriers of genetically transmitted diseases and susceptibilities.

Not only is there no logical conflict between the two principles of human improvement, but the possibility needs to be faced that, in the long run, they are mutually dependent. Obviously, the two are capable of considerable independent variation. Some social change is possible without genetic change, and probably the reverse is true. There has apparently been very little human evolution during the last 30 000 years,[1] a period during which there has been the greatest socio-cultural change. In addition, two peoples as genetically different as the Japanese and the northwest Europeans now have social systems more like each other than either is like its own prior feudal system. But one would have to be sanguine indeed to maintain that there is no limit to the independent variation of the two principles governing the human species. The evolution of an ever more complicated technology, for example, may reach an eventual plateau due to the limitations of the human brain, both in average and in extreme mental capacity. The genetic damage from nuclear weapons in the next world war may prove so great that present civilization cannot be maintained.

If both means of human change (genetic control and social reform) are potentially effective, and if they are not mutually exclusive, then the question of why one has been used to improve life and the other has not, needs an answer. Why, for instance, has the eugenics movement never left the ground? A possible answer is that genetic improvement is a long slow process, whereas social reform promises quick results. In keeping with what was said above, however, we must remember that the speed of social change is generally exaggerated. A high pro-

[1] After a rapid evolution in hominid brain size there was a sudden halt, according to Mayr. 'There has been no increase in brain size since the time of Neanderthal... nearly 100 000 years ago!' 'Cro-Magnon man, who entered history about 30 000 years ago, differs physically from modern man no more than do various modern races of man from each other.' Ernst Mayr, *Animal Species and Evolution*. Cambridge: Harvard University Press, 1963, pp. 652, 654.

portion of what passes for social reform tends to prevent rather than to induce long-run social change. Social reform efforts are like mutations; most of them are disfunctional and therefore lethal or short-lived. Since the parts of a society, like an organism, are interlinked, even a successful solution of one social problem often ultimately defeats itself by creating one or more unforeseen and unendurable new problems. On the other hand, the slowness of induced genetic change is commonly exaggerated. Some of the quickest results of scientific breeding are achieved in the first generation,[2] which can hardly be said of most successful social reforms or revolutions. It is therefore not certain that as a general rule social reform is speedier than genetic reform. The relative speed doubtless depends upon the particular goal desired. We are entitled to suspect then that the use of the alleged general rule of relative slowness as an argument against eugenics is a rationalization. The real source of antagonism to the genetic control of human beings may lie elsewhere.

Other common explanations of why human genetic control has never been seriously tried may be dismissed as patent rationalizations. It is alleged, for example, that the science of genetics is not sufficiently developed to make genetic control feasible, but animals and plants were successfully bred long before Mendelian genetics was born.[3] Again, it is alleged that

[2] Total suppression of reproduction among all individuals affected by a single-factor, autosomal, dominant genotype (DD or Dd) would lead to elimination of the genotype from the next generation (ignoring the small influence of mutation). If a constant fraction k is suppressed in reproduction, the number of affected individuals in n generations is kn (again ignoring mutation), which means that the biggest percentage drop in affected individuals will occur in the first generation. Curt Stern, *Principles of Human Genetics*, 2nd ed. San Francisco: Freeman, 1960, pp. 650–657.

[3] 'Animal breeding has long abandoned all attempts to discover superior genes individually. In fact, such desirable economic features as high egg production in chickens or high milk output in diary cows are exceedingly

human beings cannot agree on the traits they consider desirable. This is true, but they cannot agree on anything; failure to agree does not prevent their stating and enforcing rules that provide social control and stability.[4] Actually, there is more agreement on human traits considered desirable than on many other matters.[5]

My view is that the main reason why human genetic control has never been seriously tried lies in the stability factors of the socio-cultural system. It does not lie in the slowness of genetic change, in the paucity of genetic knowledge, or in the lack of consensus. It lies rather in the stubborn resistance to change inherent in human societies. In other words, eugenics is itself a social movement. Before it can be effective genetically, it has to be effective socially. It has a double barrier to cross, because it combines in a peculiar way the two systems of transmission in the human species. The changes in society that would be required to succeed in a program of human genetic control would be so fundamental that they would tend to dwarf all previous social revolutions. The socially transmitted sentiments and behavior patterns that would have to be disturbed are so deep in the minds of all of us that any imagined escape from them seems either horrible, paradoxical, or ridiculous, because they turn into pure means the things that we conceive to be ultimates.

difficult to analyze, not only genetically but even physiologically. All sorts of generalized factors, such as resistance to disease, superior utilization of food, and so forth, contribute largely to the goal of selection.' Mayr, *op. cit.*, p. 661.

[4] Laws are enforced, for example, which deprive nearly everyone of income, which prevent the practice of birth control, which give tax exemption to religious establishments, which prevent people from purchasing alcoholic beverages, which prevent people from adopting children – despite the fact that a high proportion of people in places where such laws are found are in disagreement with them.

[5] See the list of what 'most of us would value' in C.O. Carter, *Human Heredity*. Baltimore: Penguin Books, 1962, pp. 245–246.

The argument for my view can scarcely be conclusive, but certain lines of evidence and inference can be brought to bear which, to me at least, seem convincing. In general, consideration of the matter must proceed by analyzing the interrelations between the social system on the one hand and genetic change on the other.

Intended versus unintended genetic control

Since men live in a socio-cultural environment, their genetic make-up is inevitably shaped by the long-run continuities and discontinuities in this environment. Overwhelmingly, however, the effects of socio-cultural patterns on heredity are not only unforeseen but also unrealized. They are the consequences of behavior patterns which people either do not perceive or else construe as being for purposes having nothing to do with heredity. Thus people are not normally aware of statistical regularities in their mating patterns. When age at marriage is mentioned, they think of the 'legal age'. When selection of partners is mentioned, they think of their personal tastes and do not realize the trait homogamy and the geographical propinquity that characterize the mating of the population in general. They are reasonably aware of the laws and customs pertaining to marital selection but not aware of the genetic effects of these norms or of the effects of behavioral regularities existing independently of norms.

So the great bulk of social influences on genetic change have to be sharply distinguished from deliberate genetic control. Indeed, these influences are so unconscious that, like the grammar of language, they have to be studied carefully before people can be brought to realize what they are doing. However, it is precisely these social factors which give rise to most of the problems that make us regard genetic control as desirable.

A typical argument for genetic control takes the following form: a given social pattern is resulting in hereditary selection that may prove unfortunate in its consequences; therefore, some special effort must be made – that is, some control measure must be adopted – to alter the pattern in question. Usually the genetic consequences are inferred from the social practice itself, without satisfactory independent evidence (*e.g.* with respect to traits which, like general intelligence, are polygenic in character). But in other instances – e.g. with respect to the gene-diffusion role of medical success among sufferers or carriers of single-gene diseases – the biological evidence may be substantial. Occasionally, there are utopian arguments for eugenics that do not refer to any specific social pattern or genetic consequence, but see an entire eugenic paradise ahead if good heredity is made the prime goal of human endeavor. In any case the arguments for genetic control all rest on the belief that the existing sociocultural environment, either in whole or in part, is resulting in a pattern of genetic selection that is less desirable than could be achieved by deliberate effort.

This view clearly implies that remedial action is possible, despite a common semantic confusion over 'the survival of the fittest'. By definition, those biological strains that expand their numbers most rapidly are 'best adapted' to their environment. Such 'fitness', however, is purely descriptive; it has no evaluative significance nor any predictive power. It does not mean that the strain in question is 'most desirable' or that it will prove 'most fit' in the future. Logically, we are at perfect liberty to say that we do not like certain hereditary traits currently being diffused in the population, and to take measures to stop or reduce such diffusion. We can deliberately alter existing conditions in any realm in which we get control, biological as well as social. If human selection now favors carriers of genes we consider undesirable, this present 'fitness' does not prevent our altering the conditions of selection in such a way as to make the same genes 'unfit'. We can obviously alter selection in order to get genetic results we like instead of results we dislike, just as we do in other matters. We never accept the status quo as *necessarily* desirable or inescapable, simply because it is the status quo. If the actual course of events fits our desires, we do not disturb it, but if it does not do so, we intervene. Obviously, since our intervention requires both resources and knowledge, it does not always succeed, but we do manage widely to utilize natural principles to reach our goals. 'Nature' does not compel us to continue a socio-cultural environment which, in propping up or correcting the defective phenotype, inadvertently gives survival power to the myopic, stupid, diabetic, deaf, schizophrenic, etc. genotype. In altering the selective system we may wish to be humane (no one wants to deny insulin to the diabetic or forego correction of pyloric stenosis), but to save the defective and yet pay no attention to their reproduction is shortsighted, because it favors the present generation at the expense of many future ones.

Once the semantic red herring of 'fitness' is out of the way, our discussion can focus on a real problem: if a part of the social system is bringing about a result felt to be deleterious, then another part (some control apparatus) will have to be created to correct it. But the fact that the deleterious practices form a part of the existing social system indicates that they control the behavior of the very population which presumably is being asked to change them. In India, for example, the forces motivating a parent to marry off his daughters at any cost, regardless of their condition, help to keep defective traits in the gene pool;[6] but since this parental obligation is an integral part of a wider social order, it cannot be changed overnight. The Indian parent will not alter his behavior toward his daughter's

[6] In the 1961 Indian census, 99.3% of all women aged 35–39 had been married, contrasted with 93.9% in the United States in 1960 and 89.6% in France in 1962.

marriage simply because of its genetic effect on the population. He is not worried about the gene pool, but about the opinion of his neighbors, relatives, and caste-mates; he is concerned with meeting his religious and kinship obligations. In the same way, the obligation of a husband in the United States to prevent his wife from committing adultery, the stipulation in every state that adultery is a ground for divorce, and the rest of the apparatus for discouraging adultery – including even opposition to artificial insemination with sperm from a donor – these controls are not likely to be set aside in the interest of genetic improvement.

Too often the obstacle to some recommended social change is thought of as simply an attitude. People are said to be 'prejudiced', or to have some 'irrational fear' or a 'religious belief'. The remedy is then equally simple – it is to 'change people's attitude' by suitable propaganda, advertising, or education. (This is now known as the Madison Avenue approach.) But, unfortunately, battles are not won by psychological warfare alone. The motivation for conduct is determined by economic interests, social rewards and penalties, political pressures, organic needs, group loyalties, force and the threat of force – all structured in an ongoing and complex social milieu. It follows that no fundamental change in social behavior will be accomplished simply by changing the attitude; or, to put it more accurately, no change of attitude will prove possible unless the social and economic conditions causing the attitude are changed.[7]

[7] We are most aware of the inability of attitudes to account for behavior when physiological drives are involved. For instance, few believe that giving up smoking is merely a matter of increased knowledge or a changed attitude. But when it comes to social pressures, we are less perceptive. Many believe, for example, that Catholics do not use appliance methods of birth control because their theology opposes it. Yet in the United States fecund couples married over ten years use such methods in about half the cases. Ronald Freedman *et al.*, *Family Planning, Sterility and Population Growth.* New York:

In the case of genetic control it is clear that the parts of the social system that would have to be changed are especially resistant to alteration. This can be seen when we realize that the social structures most relevant to genetics are those having to do with health and medical practices on the one hand and with marriage and the family on the other. These govern respectively the two processes involved in biological selection – mortality and reproduction. In both cases extremely strong motivation is encountered – in the first because good health and physical survival are at stake, and in the second because the institutions governing sexual expression, pregnancy, and childrearing are involved.

On the medical side, it is precisely the success of the social controls tending to maximize survival that is producing genetic trends that many people find alarming. In India in 1911–1921 the death rate was such that only 38% of the males born would survive to age 20.[8] In the generation of white males born in the United States in 1840, 61% survived to age 20, whereas it is estimated that among those born in 1960 over 96% will live to that age.[9] In other words, not long ago in human history mortality prior to the age of reproduction was the principal mechanism for positive genetic selection in human populations. The remarkable constitution built up by this selective process forms the rich genetic inheritance that the human species is coasting on at present. Now, however, to all intents and purposes, selection on the basis of differential mortality has been

McGraw-Hill, 1959, p. 185. Similarly, polls have shown a majority of Americans opposed to married women working; yet about a third of our married women are in the labor force. Economic pressures are often more powerful motivators than sheer attitudes or preferences.

[8] Kingsley Davis, *Population of India and Pakistan*. Princeton: Princeton University Press, 1951, p. 240.

[9] Paul H. Jacobson, 'Cohort Survival for Generations since 1840,' *Milbank Memorial Fund Quarterly*, 42 (July 1964), pp. 44–45.

eliminated, because virtually nobody dies before the reproductive period and very few before the end of it. Jacobson estimates that among the white females born in 1960 in the United States, 96% will survive to age 45.

The social controls yielding such complete success in non-selectivity are so strong that there appears no possibility whatever of changing them. The state laws of this nation, for example, do not even permit abortion in order to prevent a genetically damaged child from being born; it seems unlikely that permitting death after birth will be tolerated. Instead, we can confidently expect that the proportion of defective phenotypes in the population will continue to rise – because the excess mortality once characterizing such defectives has all but disappeared.

If this conclusion is correct, then the entire burden of eugenic policy is thrown onto the reproductive side.[10] Here the formidable system of religious and moral control over sexual and family relations is encountered. An examination of what this means will prove illuminating.

Genetic control and the family

Perhaps the most fundamental obstacle to genetic control through deliberate reproductive selection lies in a curious fact. The human species, despite all its achievements in technology, has retained a very primitive mode of social organization with respect to human reproduction. It has retained a system in which people are connected socially by birth (kinship) and in which responsibility for the rearing of children is primarily given to those who biologically engender them. In some ways, indeed,

[10] We are now speaking of selection only. There is, of course, another aspect of eugenic policy, which is that of minimizing radiation and other causes of predominantly deleterious mutations.

the form that this system takes in modern industrial society is more elementary than it is in primitive communities, for in the latter there is often a highly institutionalized and fictional quality in extended kin relations and frequently a lack of concern with whether or not a child is biologically 'one's own'.

In industrial societies the elementary unit – the nuclear family, consisting of the reproducing pair (the parents) and their own offspring (the children) – stands out. It is about as simple as a familial mode of reproduction can be made, and yet it is the means by which the most complex human societies replace themselves. There is a serious question, however, as to whether or not it is too frail a vehicle for the duties it is asked to perform. Certainly, under the conditions of an industrial open-class society, it appears to function in a dysgenic way.

In a primitive situation – that is, in a hunting and gathering economy, which prevailed throughout most human history – the cultural apparatus was not elaborate enough to mediate greatly between the individual organism and his physical environment. Since mortality in early life was very high, the burden of genetic selection did not fall very heavily on the reproductive side. But even with respect to reproduction, the family system did a fair job of favorable breeding. It did so primarily by a slight complication of the family unit – namely, polygyny.[11] This practice meant that the most successful males sired a disproportionately large share of the next generation.

[11] There is considerable confusion in ethnographic literature over the meaning of polygyny. The confusion seems mainly to stem from thinking of societies as being synonymous with 'a culture', or a set of 'customs'. By this conception, if the society 'allows' polygyny, it is 'polygynous'. However, the fact that a social system 'allows' something does not make it prevalent, nor does the fact that it does not "allow" something make it non-existent. Thus India permits people to be millionaires, but there are not many millionaires in India. Latin American countries do not 'permit' polygyny (at least in their official religious and legal machinery), but a significant

Polygyny persisted with amazing tenacity. It is found in most agrarian societies today, including Latin American countries and virtually the whole of Africa. However, as the Neolithic revolution spread widely throughout the world, the human species was able to put a much more elaborate cultural technology between itself and the non-cultural environment. The selective value of polygyny accordingly changed character. With the domestication of plants and animals, the successful male was not necessarily the keen-eyed and swift hunter, but perhaps the myopic schemer, the social manipulator, and the inheritor of property. Furthermore, the second and third mates (whether wives or concubines) tended to be drawn from the less advantaged economic strata, with unknown effects on genetic selection, if any.

In industrial societies there has doubtless been an increase in plural mating, but the further development of technology – in this case contraception and abortion – has freed such mating from procreation and hence from genetic significance. Not only has birth control changed the character of plural mating, but the tendency of industrial societies to sheer off kinship bonds beyond the nuclear family (a tendency associated with vertical and

portion of Latin American men have more than one woman who is bearing children to them. We are referring to *de facto* polygyny, regardless of whether or not it is *de jure*. Unfortunately, it is easier to get information on what people in a society say 'should' be done than to get data on what they actually do. But even on an ethical basis, C.S. Ford and E.A. Beach (*Patterns of Sexual Behavior*. New York: Harper, 1951, p. 108) found that in 84% of their sample of 185 societies 'men are permitted by custom to have more than one mate at a time.' Similarly, Murdock found in his sample of societies that 193 permitted and encouraged polygyny and only 43 did not. See P. Murdock, *Social Structure*. New York: Macmillan, 1949, p. 28. There is no warrant that I know of for the statement by Mayr, *op. cit.*, p. 651, that 'most cases of polygyny among contemporary peoples were... secondarily derived from a preceding monogamy.'

geographic mobility in a competitive social structure) has also applied to stable secondary sexual unions. Enduring unions involving an otherwise married man and giving rise to children have therefore become rare in advanced countries. How this has come about can be understood in terms of the changing interrelation between the family and the rest of the social order as modern society emerged. With the shift of production from the home to the factory or office, the economic value of the housewife declined. A wife remained financially valuable only if she ceased to be merely a housewife – that is, if she entered the outside labor force; but if she did that, she received remuneration of her own and thus acquired independence. Furthermore, with the opening up of jobs to women on an individual basis, regardless of their marital status, women no longer had to form an enduring sexual union with a man in order to gain an adequate livelihood. They were therefore, even when they came from the lower classes, not forced to accept a secondary or tertiary marital or concubinal relationship with a male. They could either remain unattached or marry a relatively unsuccessful male and help him out by participating in the labor force. In turn the first wife was more independent and thus less likely to tolerate her husband's taking a second mate. At the same time, the man found that a second wife or concubine had less and less utility to him. She was not productive; the value of her children was virtually nil, again because production had largely shifted from the home and because an education was increasingly required; and sexual gratification was possible without a durable legal commitment to the woman and without her bearing children. For these reasons the marginal utility of a second mate, in relation to the cost and trouble, became negative.

Monogamy, death control, and family planning

The closer the economy is to subsistence, the more selective it is from the standpoint of traits adapted to the physical, or non-cultural, environment. Under polygynous conditions the economically successful male not only sired more children but more of them survived. The latter was true under monogamous conditions as well, but with the improved control of mortality in the nineteenth century, the number of living children in the household rose to an unpredented average. This, together with the increased cost of children on the one hand and their growing disutility except as playthings and ego surrogates on the other, led to the use of birth control. The result was that the ambitious man and woman, instead of contributing more than their share to the next generation, contributed a lesser share. Their aspirations were higher for themselves and their children, and their knowledge and use of birth control techniques were superior to those of the less successful. The class differences in fertility began to widen noticeably in the latter half of the nineteenth century in the industrializing countries, reached their greatest spread sometime around the turn of the century, depending upon the circumstances of the particular nation, and eventually (most noticeably during the period of the baby boom after the great depression) began to contract. In 1910 in the United States, for instance, the highest occupational class, the professional, had a cumulative reproductive performance, among its married women with husband present, which was 58% of that of the lowest class, unskilled laborers. By 1940 the ratio was still about the same, 55%, but by 1952 it had risen to 69%. Furthermore, in 1952 the lowest fertility was no longer found in professional families but in those of clerical and sales workers.[12] By 1957 the

[12] Charles F. Westoff, 'Differential Fertility in the United States: 1900 to 1952', *American Sociological Review*, 19 (October 1954), p. 558.

ratio of professional to unskilled married fertility had risen to 72%.[13]

The class differentials have thus declined in magnitude, and with the shift to lowest levels among the middle strata, the inverse correlation of reproduction with occupational status has become less pronounced. This is particularly true when success within the broad occupational or educational strata is analysed, for then it is often found that success and fertility are positively correlated.[14]

There is no reason to believe that the inverse correlation between fertility and social status will soon completely reverse itself, despite wishful thinking to that effect. The reason is that one of the conditions supporting the inverse relationship is not likely to change – namely, the factor of greater aspiration among those who are in, or rise to, the upper social strata. Even though birth control techniques may become so simple that anybody, no matter how inefficient, can control births, it may still remain true that those who count on getting ahead in life and having their children do so will, on the average, have fewer offspring. Further, the family allowance schemes that many countries now have – *e.g.* Canada, France, Belgium, Sweden – tend, if they increase fertility at all, to have more effect upon those in poor than on those in good circumstances, because the lower the income the higher the ratio of the child-allowance to it. Progressive income taxes, liberal welfare schemes, increased preva-

[13] Clyde V. Kiser, 'Differential Fertility in the United States' in National Bureau of Economic Research, *Demographic and Economic Change in Developed Countries*. Princeton: Princeton University Press, 1960, p. 105.

[14] A brief summary of relevant studies is contained in Cedric O. Carter, 'Changing Patterns of Differential Fertility in Northwest Europe and in North America', *Eugenics Quarterly*, 9 (September 1962), pp. 147–150. The research literature on differential fertility by occupation, income, and education is enormous. The quickest guide to it is the section on 'Differential Fertility' in the bibliographic quarterly, *Population Index*.

lence of premarital conception among juveniles, ease of youthful marriages, quick cure of venereal diseases, and subsidized housing for lower-income groups – all of these characteristics of contemporary society are conducive to a negative relationship between socioeconomic status and fertility. There are of course factors pushing in the opposite direction. To a certain extent children have become items of conspicuous consumption which the better-off can afford. Also, children are easier to care for if the family can afford to live in spatious suburbs and to withdraw the wife completely from the labor force. No one knows for sure what will happen in the future, but I would expect that approximately the present situation will continue for some time – that is, that reproduction will be highest at the two ends of the socioeconomic scale and lowest among those in the middle who are too educated to have children carelessly and too poor to have them abundantly. In the meantime, in the majority of the world which is still groping toward a modern social system, the class differences in fertility will probably become greater before they become smaller again.

Democracy and the right to reproduce

Not only does the small nuclear family, as affected by the rest of industrial society, fail to produce unintended positive genetic selection, but it also militates against policies deliberately aimed at genetic control. This can be seen in the curious polarization of modern life. In most primitive and archaic agrarian systems there is a great deal of economics in household and kinship groups (because these are still productive organizations) and a great deal of companionship in other work groups, because these are stabilized and traditional. In our type of society, however, the economic and professional world is so much involved with rapidly changing technology that work-relationships are competitive and instable. Individuals must be emotionally prepared to break bonds easily, to start life again in a new neighborhood or community, to deal with a new boss, etc. Even the physical surroundings change so rapidly that attachment to the place where one grew up is attachment to only a memory.

My purpose is not to condemn these societal traits. They are simply the features of societies that have a high level of living. But the traits do clearly throw the burden of strong and continued campanionship, of mutual trust and personal dependence, upon the nuclear family. Male friendships tend to be superficial and ephemeral. A man confides his personal feeling to his 'girl-friend' or his wife, not to his male companions who are usually his business associates and therefore also his competitors. The husband-wife bond is therefore given tremendous strength. Similarly, the parent-child bond receives strong emphasis as a personal relationship. Children are the only human beings over whom the parents have personal as distinct from economic control, and for the child the parents are ordinarily the only stable personal anchor in a world of changeable relationships and procedures.

As a consequence, contemporary society powerfully impels people into marriage and parenthood. 'Going steady' at a tender age, a drop in the average age at marriage throughout the industrialized world, and early childbearing are overt manifestations of this impulsion. Inevitably the ethical feeling arises that marriage and procreation are somehow inalienable rights. The personal identity with 'one's own child' has the implication (doubtless reinforced by the popularization of genetics) that a child should, if at all possible, be biologically one's own.

Thus we reach a result surprisingly like the past. In the Medieval system, or in any traditional agrarian society, the institutional structure was such as to motivate people to marry and to produce many births. The structure reflected past millenia in which any social system that survived had somehow to compensate for a high death rate. But the family and reproduction were so intertwined with the economic and class system that marriage was not necessarily considered an inalienable right of every person regardless of his condition. In Medieval Europe a precondition was personal command of the means of support for a wife and family.[15] Nowadays, with democratic individualism, the peculiar and unique benefits of the family are felt to be everybody's birth-right. Birth control is taken for granted, but it is not used either to produce only enough children to replace the population or to improve the genetic inheritance or environmental opportunities of the next generation. It is used instead to have as many children as the couple personally want under existing conditions, regardless of future demographic or genetic effects. By this system nearly everybody gets married at a relatively young age when economic conditions permit. In the United States in 1960, the median age for brides at first marriage was 20.1; for grooms, 23.1; and the proportion of women aged 35 to 39 who had ever been married was 94%. Furthermore, the degree of standardization in number of children per family has reached a point never before achieved in human history. In 1960 in the United States, among all families with a head aged 35 to 44, nearly half – 46.4% – had two or three children under 18 years of age. In the Philippines in 1958, on the other hand, among ever-married women aged 35 to 44, the maximum proportion in any two orders of living children was about 30%, which was approximately the proportion having five or six living children.[16]

[15] Josiah C. Russel, 'Demographic Values in the Middle Ages', in Geo. F. Mair, ed., *Studies in Population*, Princeton: Princeton University Press, 1949, p. 104; *British Medieval Population*, Albuquerque: University of New Mexico Press, 1948, pp. 154–164. Geo. C. Homans, *English Villagers of the Thirteenth Century*, Cambridge: Harvard University Press, 1941, ch. 10.
[16] In backward countries with relatively high mortality and high fertility, the size of family varies greatly. For this there are several reasons: there is little or no medical treatment for low fecundity on the one side and not much

Obviously, to the extent that the variation is not random with respect to genetic factors, one can see how much more selective the system is in underdeveloped as against the highly standardized and culturally successful developed countries. Further effects

birth limitation on the other. Also, the factors governing mortality tend to strike some families more than others. In advanced countries, however, couples nearly all aim to have *some* children, hence seek treatment for sterility or low fecundity, but they limit their offspring after they have had their desired number, and the desired number tends to be a common standard. Furthermore, since few people die during childhood, the mortality factor is nearly constant as among families. The following figures illustrate the difference:

Country and category of those who have had at least one child	Percentage having the following number of living children							
	1	2	3	4	5	6–9	10+	Total
Tanganyka, Asian Population, 1957								
Ever-married women aged 35–44	6.5	9.5	13.4	16.0	16.0	36.9	1.8	100.0
Philippines, 1958								
Ever-married women aged 35–44	6.0	7.9	11.3	14.2	16.4	42.7	1.5	100.0
Hungary, 1945								
Married women aged 35–44	29.4	31.9	17.6	9.4	5.3	6.3	0.1	100.0
United States, 1960								
All heads of families aged 43–44	22.4	32.4	22.4	22.7*				

Data are from United Nations *Demographic Yearbook* 1959, table 7, except those for the United States which are from Census of 1960, US Summary–Detailed Characteristics, table 186, p. 1–463. The last percentage for the United States* is for 4 *or more* children.

follow from the reduction in births per family. If the average age at marriage remains constant or is reduced, the lower fertility will mean that a greater proportion of all births will occur to younger rather than to older mothers. This reduces the incidence of congenitive disorders, most of which occur more frequently at higher parities and to older mothers and fathers, *e.g.* Rh-erythroblastosis, Down's syndrome (mongolism), twinning, hydrocephaly, cleft palate. In general, the reason for the higher incidence is that the older the parents the longer they have had for mutations to develop in their reproductive cells. See Eimatsunaga, 'Measures Affecting Population Trends and Possible Genetic Consequences', *World Population Conference* (Belgrade, 1965).

Given the traits just discussed – the emphasis on the nuclear family as the personal unit in modern society, the feeling that everyone has a right to marry and procreate some children of his own, the insistence that everybody be kept alive at any cost – we see little likelihood of a new positive system of genetic control arising soon in industrialized societies.

Significantly, geneticists and others shy away from the notion of 'compulsion' in regard to any restraint on reproduction. There is of course compulsion in *promoting* reproduction. Laws against abortion compel pregnant women to bear a child even against their wishes; laws against birth control forbid couples to acquire contraceptive materials or information or to become sterilized even when they wish to do so; laws against divorce force some couples to stay married against their wishes; laws taxing bachelors and/or using tax money for family allowances compel people at large to favor parenthood. But when compulsion is suggested for wise *limitation* of childbearing, it tends to be rejected out-of-hand by official policy – sometimes with thundering ecclesiastical denunciation, sometimes with ridicule. When, for example, someone suggests that couples be licensed to bear children, he is generally ridiculed, because the idea runs counter to habitual sentiments. Yet marriage is, in essence, a license to bear children. Its only peculiarity is that it gives an unlimited franchise and it is easier to get than almost any other kind of license – far easier than a driver's license, a beer or a hunting license. About the only sense of restraint ever attached to it is a quantitative one: some people feel that a couple should have no more than the number of children they can support and rear adequately. This, however, is only a 'should', with no enforcement contemplated, and many who hold this view would severely limit the means available. Furthermore, there is an equal or greater emphasis on the treatment of sterility, on the ground that every couple should have at least two children.

The whole question of reproduction is thus surrounded by a mystique that places it beyond control for collective purposes. This appears in many ways. Physicians, for example, commonly violate their medical ethics with regard to contraception, for they prescribe, not the method that would be best for the patient, but the method that 'his religion permits', which may in fact be tragically ineffective. Our state laws forbidding induced abortion for eugenic or birth control purposes guarantee the murder and maiming of an unknown but substantial number of women each year. Our sex and family instruction in schools is so unrealistic and so divorced from secular considerations of collective welfare that it is grotesque. If we cannot find ways to avoid the personal tragedies represented by high rates of premarital pregnancy, illegitimate births, ill-advised marriages, unwanted children, and veneral disease, we are not likely to find a way to improve, or even save from decay, the genetic constitution of future generations.

To say that a system of eugenic control is *theoretically* possible or conceivable is one thing. To say that it can *actually* be put into practice is another. I reach the conclusion that the existing reproductive institutions, despite some variation, make it unlikely that people will soon start controlling themselves genetically, although such control is theoretically possible. An effective system of eugenic control would involve profound changes in the very web of relations that organizes and expresses the personal lives of moderns. It would overthrow the existing system of emotional rewards and punishments, the present interpretations of reality, the familiar links between the person and social status.

Most people therefore, even when they favor eugenics, do not wish to reform our reproductive institutions for eugenic purposes. At most they want to make only small changes that will leave the basic family system intact. For instance, a familiar proposal is the provision of genetic counseling services, to inform couples of the probabilities of gross genetic defects in their prospective offspring. This would be a humane effort which no more achieves genetic control than the use of contraception for private purposes achieves population control.

Eugenic utopias

It is of course easy to imagine social arrangements that would make genetic control possible. Eugenic utopias have been extant since Plato's *Republic*. The modern ones, such as Muller's *Out of the Night* and Aldous Huxley's *Brave New World*, do not require remarkable imagination on the scientific side, because advanced technology for genetic control is already available or obviously soon will be. More imagination is required in conjecturing the social arrangements required to utilize these techniques, but even this can be done with ease in one's armchair. Very often the social changes are slighted in the eugenic literature, for reasons we shall presently explain, but not because of inability to imagine these changes. Whether serious or satirical, one can conjure up any kind of society one wishes, but one cannot demonstrate that it will work or show how to start it.

A first step in the construction of a eugenic utopia is to decide whether the entire population, or merely an elite, is to have its heredity improved. If the elite idea is favored, then obviously the society cannot be democratic. Either the hereditary elite would rule by virtue of its superior birth (the antithesis of democracy), or it would be governed by the hereditary riff-raff (a paradoxical disproof of the controlled-hereditary idea).[17]

A second step is easier: it is to imagine a social adjustment whereby those having their heredity controlled (whether an elite or the whole population) would have no preference for their children, in the sense of genetically their 'own'. This change of attitude could presumably be accomplished by educating couples to welcome a child which comes from artificial insemination or, better, from an implanted fertilized ovum. In the latter case the child would be genetically derived from a male and female who were superior to the couple, but it would be born to the 'mother', would be nurtured by her, and would consequently be emotionally identified with her. The parents would thus regard the child as their own – much as a purchased house or car becomes a source of pride to its new owners, regardless of the fact that they themselves did not manufacture it. The nation could maintain a board of geneticists to determine who should furnish the sperm and the ova and what crosses should be made in the artificial mating. Needless to say, the males not required to supply sperm to the official 'sperm-banks' would all be sterilized, and the women not supplying ova would

[17] R.A. McConnell, like Aldous Huxley, depicts an elite system of genetic control. 'The Absolute Weapon', *American Institute of Biological Sciences Bulletin*, II (June 1961), pp. 14–16. It is interesting that when authors in liberal societies wish to satirize genetic control, they depict the eugenic utopia as composed of hereditary castes; when they are serious about it, they depict the utopia as democratic. McConnell assumes that the nation adopting genetic control is the USSR, a strategem which allows him to make the elitest assumption but which is not very realistic in view of the strong Communist antithesis to the idea of human hereditary control.

have their own ovulation either suppressed or diverted. The board of supervising geneticists would have confidential records on the pedigree of all persons born in the population, as well as records of their traits and achievements. On this basis it would determine who is to be sterilized and who is to furnish sperm or ova.

Such a scheme would keep marriage and the family as a means of rearing children, and so would do minimum violence to traditional social structure. There seems no inherent reason why genetic control would require further social reorganization. However, it is worth noting that those who furnish sperm and ova would possibly have some sort of a special status in society. They would not be sterilized, hence their families could be normal in our sense but abnormal in the new community. In this case, since they would necessarily be persons of high status, their type of family would tend to be regarded as something highly prized. There might be a drive on the part of others (necessarily the vast majority) to have families of the prized sort, and since they would be smart – *i.e.* highly bred themselves – they might be able to win out in this regard. On the other hand, this inequality would be avoided by requiring all children to be artificially conceived. In any event the society would require tight control to enforce the eugenic system. This would be particularly true if human breeding were used to produce diverse types in the population for special tasks, somewhat analogous to the division of labor in insect societies.

Further, there seems to be, in our imaginary society, an imbalance between the degree of science used in breeding and the readiness to allow the average couple to rear children in the next generation. Recalling that the individual is a product of his socialization (especially early in life) as well as his heredity, a society capable of dictating the genetic constitution of future generations seems hardly likely to neglect their culturally transmitted make-up. For this reason it may not regard all couples as equally fit to rear children. Although modern research is giving a greater role to maternal love and attention in personality development than was formerly recognized, the fact remains that professional child-rearers – trained, and perhaps even bred, for the task – might be superior. Once this happened, there would be little reason for encouraging stable marriage and family life. A sizable proportion of women would be required to serve as maternal host for bearing a number of offspring. Other women would be freed from this duty but might nevertheless be professional child-rearers. The sterilized men would be free to enter any kind of relations that suited them. The sperm- and ova-bearers, however, would have to be carefully regulated, perhaps allowed to mate among themselves, but not necessarily allowed to rear children. Obviously, under these conditions, marriage and the family as we know them might cease altogether. With sexual behavior divorced from reproduction, why regulate it at all? With reproduction divorced from child-rearing, why build up an identity between two 'parents' (male and female) and their 'offspring'? If social identity is necessary for children, they can be emotionally attached to one or more professional child-rearers. Presumably the relations among any set of child-rearers would not be complicated by sexual possessiveness, preoccupation with pregnancy, the necessity of coping with children of disparate ages, etc. The business of socialization, like the business of genetic selection, could thus be rationalized along scientific lines, utilizing an intelligent division of labor.

The more one pursues such speculations the clearer it is that they are of little value. They do not, for example, enable us to predict the kind of social system required for genetic control. The uncertainty pertains not so much to the immediate adjustments (these are fairly straightforward) as to the wider ramifications of those adjustments. It is like predicting the effects of new weapons in warfare. One can assess the probable costs, technical personnel, and physical damage fairly well, but wider effects like the reception by public opinion at home and abroad and the repercussion on relations between the military and the civilian sectors are hard to forecast.

Furthermore, speculation on the nature of a eugenic utopia does not answer the question of how we move from here to there. How do we start? What are the immediate social changes that must be made, and how can they be put into effect? Although social reform presumably requires a vision of what the ultimate result will be, this vision need not be highly detailed. It is more effective if the basic principle is grasped but detailed attention is focussed on merely the first step or two. In the case of genetic control we are so far away from even a semblance of it that utopian speculation seems particularly idle. Furthermore, since such speculation does lie so far in the future (since it is so 'visionary') and since it inevitably offends certain sentiments supporting our received institutions, anyone who takes it seriously tends to be penalized in various ways, either by ridicule or by threats and denunciation. Most sensible people, not wishing to incur such penalites for a patently distant cause, forego serious advocacy of radical eugenic measures. This leaves the field to cranks – *i.e.* to persons so fanatic on the subject that they are willing to throw caution to the wind. Other than cranks, it is only persons who have already established a sound reputation on other grounds, such as Herman J. Muller, who dare to advocate a system of positive genetic control. The so-called eugenics movement therefore has the alternative of either playing safe and advocating only mild measures (*e.g.* voluntary counseling) or of being bold and shooting for a genetic utopia. Up to now it appears that the movement has generally taken the first course: it is respectable but almost totally ineffective. Occasional expressions of eugenic radicalism tend to be ignored unless they come from some prominent figure or achieve literary distinction.[18]

[18] Denatured respectability was conferred on the eugenics movement by

Is genetic control sociologically possible?

My purpose in discussing the sociological obstacles is not to suggest that genetic control is impossible. It is rather to show that human beings are still a long way from such self control. A species which cannot as yet even control its own sheer numbers is obviously not likely to control its own genetic constitution. Doubtless small eugenic measures are feasible. Something will perhaps be accomplished within the next fifty years by dissemination of knowledge about specific genetic diseases and

Frederick Osborn in *Preface to Eugenics* (New York: Harper), first published in 1940 and revised in 1951. As an illustration of how this was done, one can cite (pp. 241–242) the three steps he proposed for 'the development of a program of positive eugenics:

(1) General improvement of the environment...

(2) Establishment of conditions which will equalize the extent to which all parents are in a position to choose freely how many children they will have...

(3) Finally, the introduction of eugenic measures of a psychological and cultural sort which will tend to encourage births among responsible parents most susceptible to the stimulus of their environment, and to diminish births among those least capable of adjusting themselves to their environment...'

In an era when the Nazis in Germany had made genetic control synonymous with racism in the eyes of most intellectuals, Osborn was apparently trying to deflect hostility by borrowing the ideology of 'environmentalism' and conferring it illogically on eugenics. He reached the comforting conclusion that democracy, individualism, and freedom will automatically provide beneficial genetic control. He thus evaded the problem of authority and discipline altogether, but aligned eugenics on the side of liberal dogma, denaturing the movement in the process.

As an example of how serious discussions of genuine genetic control must be disguised as non-serious, one can take the article by McConnell previously cited. It is presented as a fictional account of a non-existent Soviet policy written in 1975!

their control through genetic counseling and selective birth control. But there seems no indication that such limited measures will evolve into a comprehensive scheme for selective human breeding that will substantially raise the average level of genetic capacities in the population or greatly increase the proportion having abilities now defined as superior. This would require such fundamental changes in reproductive institutions and control systems that it appears unlikely as an evolutionary process.

However, social change occurs not only by gradual evolution but also by a saltatory process – revolution. It is possible to imagine a catastrophe so great that it would spark a eugenic transformation in one or more advanced nations. To do so, it would have to be, of course, a genetic crisis, and the only one that suggests itself is one produced by the use of nuclear weapons in a third World War. As Professor Glass' discussion of possible effects shows, such wholesale radiation could present a genetic crisis of a new and frightening kind to mankind. Under such circumstances, faced with generations burdened with countless horrifying mutations, nations possessed of modern genetic science would be likely to overcome all traditional obstacles in favor of a comprehensive genetic control system. It is even possible that the public at large would exaggerate the potential harm of such widespread irradiation, making control measures seem all the more desirable. Public support for eugenic measures has come mainly from concern over the manifest and sometimes horrifying consequences of defective alleles of large effect. A genetic crisis of the sort mentioned would enormously multiply such horrors. This would rally public support for a eugenic program despite the fact that such a program would doubtless ultimately do more for human heredity by selecting against slightly harmful rather than extremely harmful mutants. See Mootoo Kimura, 'Recent Advances in the Theory of Population Genetics', *World Population Conference*, 1965. It is likely, too, that the catastrophe would have other effects tending to revolutionize the social order. It would initially reduce and contaminate the resources on which human beings depend, making necessary the most stringent control measures. In the longer run, by decimating the population but allowing most resources to recover rapidly, it would perhaps lower the people-to-resources ratio and thus stimulate the substitution of technology for manpower. Human societies might thus move to a new level of all-around scientific utilization, with genetic regulation as a single, though crucial, feature. With more science, the necessity of breeding people with greater intellectual capacities, to advance science itself, would become imperative. Thus the scientific control system would become self-reinforcing, carrying genetic improvements to a point hardly dreamed of today.

Once successfully adopted, genetic regulation would tend to persist even when the genetic crisis giving rise to it had passed. The reason would lie partly in the self-reinforcing nature of comprehensive scientific utilization just alluded to. It would also lie in the superiority of a society having genetic control over one not having it. Deliberate genetic control certainly appears to be the 'absolute weapon', the most powerful means for survival yet contemplated.

Conclusion: the reality versus the potential

The potential gain from systematic improvement of human inheritance seems enormous. It holds the promise of transforming human society in precisely those ways in which purely cultural change is impotent. It would revolutionize not merely the instrumentalities of life but the proclivities and limitations inherited from our long ancestry of hunters and gatherers, proclivities that are now inappropriate for the complex socio-cultural environment in which we try to live. It would reverse the present tendency to eliminate the selective bars against physical defect and mental mediocrity. It would save the species from its top-sided dependence on cultural props for biological inadequacies.

To be sure, genetic regulation, like any other human effort, runs the risk of failure. The artificially created thoroughbreds of the species might prove less viable than the mongrels. But if human effort waited on a 100% guarantee of success, we would never do anything. We already have the scientific means to make considerable improvements in human heredity, even without the biochemical interventions intimated by the discoveries which Dr Tatum has so vividly described.

The major obstacle to a program of human hereditary improvement is therefore not any lack of genetic science but the resistance inherent in the stability system of existing societies. Just how drastic the changes in reproductive and political institutions would be is impossible to say, but they would probably be so drastic that most human beings, with minds and motives formed under existing institutions, cannot even tolerate them in theory, much less in practice.

Under the circumstances, we shall probably struggle along with small measures at a time, with the remote possibility that these may eventually evolve into a genetic control system. We shall doubtless increasingly seek to restrain reproduction in those cases in which there is patently a large risk of grossly defective offspring. As more genetic anomalies are discovered, as more tests for heterozygous carriers are discovered, this procedure will grow in importance. The morality of specific techniques of applied genetics – artificial insemination, selective sterilization, ovular transplantation, eugenic abortion, genetic record-keeping, genetic testing – will be thunderously debated in theological and Marxian terms dating from past ages. Possibly, within half a century or so, this may foot up to a comprehensive program.

It seems more likely, however, that the change will be precipitated more suddenly by something new in human history, a genetic crisis. The survivors of a nuclear haulocaust might prove willing to adopt a thorough system of genetic control in order to minimize the horrifying effects of radiation on the next generations. Once the barriers inherent in the existing social organization of human life were thus broken, genetic control would probably persist because of the competitive power it would give to the societies that maintained it.

Eventually, regardless of how it comes about, human genetic control seems bound to occur, unless all progress is halted. With plant and animal breeding already well established, similar control over Homo sapiens is the logical next step. The only thing that could prevent it would be something that would stop progress in general – self-destruction of mankind or a regression into a permanent dark age.

If and when it does come, the deliberate alteration of the species for sociological purposes will be a more fateful step than any previously taken by mankind. It will dwarf three of the previous most revolutionary steps: the emergence of speech, the domestication of plants and animals, and the industrial revolution. The reason is simple: whereas these other changes were socio-cultural in character and thus subject to the limitations of man's capacities, the new development would be both socio-cultural and biological. It would, for the first time, enable man to overcome the sole limit on socio-cultural evolution, the limit set by his innate capacities. These capacities would change very slowly, and quite probably in a downhill direction, under present conditions of inadvertent selection. On the other hand, deliberate control, once begun, would soon benefit science and technology, which in turn would facilitate further hereditary improvement, which again would extend science, and so on in a self-reinforcing spiral without limit. In other words, when man has conquered his own biological evolution he will have laid the basis for conquering everything else. The universe will be his, at last.